To the past and future children

of the movement.

JANUARY 20, 2009.

WHEN MY PARENTS FOUND OUT I'D BEEN **ARRESTED** AND GONE TO JAIL, THEY WERE DEVASTATED. I WAS AN EMBARRASSMENT, A SOURCE OF HUMILIATION AND GOSSIP.

SO I STOPPED COMING HOME AS MUCH.

I STILL SAW MY FAMILY OVER THE SUMMER AND ON BREAKS HERE AND THERE, BUT **NASHVILLE**--AND THE GROWING NASHVILLE STUDENT MOVEMENT--

--BECAME MY **HOME.**

MARCH: BOOK TWO
WRITTEN BY JOHN LEWIS & ANDREW AYDIN
ART BY NATE POWELL

BY RESPECTFULLY INSISTING TO BE TREATED FAIRLY, WE WOULD DRAW ATTENTION TO THE **UNFAIRNESS** OF SEGREGATION.

MA'AM--

YES, WE'RE OPEN

may we be served, please?

SPLOOSH

I WAS BEGINNING MY SENIOR YEAR AT AMERICAN BAPTIST, AND ANY TIME NOT DEVOTED TO MY SCHOOL WORK WAS SPENT PLANNING, PREPARING, AND ORGANIZING.

FALL 1960 WAS MARKED BY A CONTENTIOUS PRESIDENTIAL ELECTION CAMPAIGN BETWEEN VICE-PRESIDENT RICHARD NIXON AND SENATOR JOHN F. KENNEDY.

KENNEDY NARROWLY WON.

BRITE-

BRITE

WHAT THAT WOULD MEAN FOR ME-- AND FOR AFRICAN-AMERICANS IN GENERAL-- I DID NOT KNOW.

FUMP

BUT OVERALL, I WAS OPTIMISTIC.

THAT NOVEMBER, WE BEGAN OUR NEW CAMPAIGN.

BUT WHAT WE FOUND, AS WE PUSHED OUR PROTESTS DEEPER INTO THE HEART OF SEGREGATED SOCIETY,

WAS THAT OUR NONVIOLENT ACTIONS

WERE MET WITH INCREASINGLY MORE VIOLENT RESPONSES.

KLIK

WHRRRRRRP

RRRRIIIINNNLLLNG!

hello?

JOHN--

YOU GOTTA COME QUICK--

THE CALL WAS FROM ONE OF OUR SPOTTERS.

--THERE'S TROUBLE AT THE KRYSTAL!

on it.

mm-hm. be right there.

well, that didn't take long.

IT WAS A FUMIGATOR.

USED ONLY FOR KILLING PESTS.

BAM!
BAM!
BAM!
BAM!
BAM!
BAM!

WE DID NOT DIE THAT DAY,

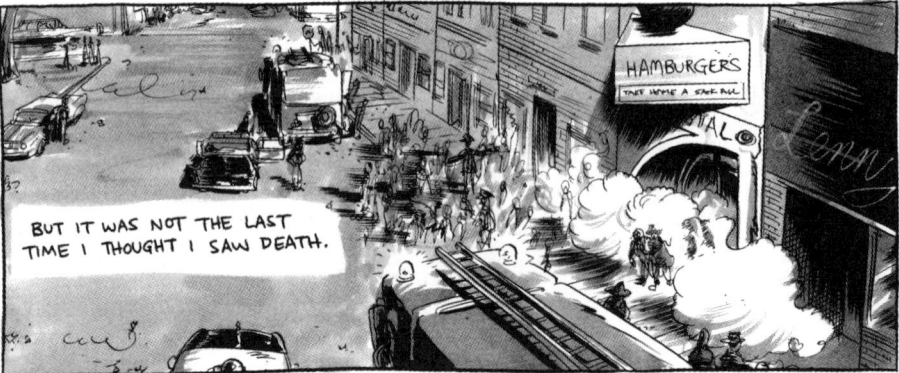

BUT IT WAS NOT THE LAST TIME I THOUGHT I SAW DEATH.

HAMBURGERS

IT WAS A CLEAR DEMONSTRATION OF THE VIOLENT FORCES **UNLEASHED** BY OUR QUEST FOR HUMAN DIGNITY.

jingle jingle

NOW SHOWING
CECIL B DEMILLE'S
THE TEN COMMANDMENTS

FEBRUARY 1961 --
NASHVILLE, TN.

one fr THE TEN COMMANDMENTS, please.

sorry next.

BUT AS THE VIOLENCE GOT WORSE, OUR PROTESTS BECAME MORE AGGRESSIVE.

CAN I HAVE ONE TICKET FOR THE TEN COMMANDMENTS, PLEASE?

I'M SORRY -- I CAN'T SELL YOU A TICKET.

WE BEGAN HOLDING "STAND-INS" AT LOCAL SEGREGATED MOVIE THEATERS.

THE TACTIC WAS BORROWED FROM STUDENTS AT THE UNIVERSITY OF TEXAS IN AUSTIN.

hi -- I'D LIKE ONE FOR THE TEN COMMANDMENTS.

SORRY -- CAN'T SELL YOU A TICKET.

next.

cn you hander this?

WHEN THEY REFUSED US, WE WOULD GET BACK IN LINE AND WAIT OUR TURN TO ASK AGAIN.

HUP TWO THREE FOUR

HUP TWO THREE FOUR

FOR MORE THAN TWO WEEKS,

WE PROTESTED EVERY NIGHT.

AT FIRST,

IT WAS JUST THE LOCAL WHITE TEENAGERS WE HAD TO WORRY ABOUT.

IN RESPONSE TO THE ESCALATING VIOLENCE, THE CENTRAL COMMITTEE HELD A MEETING THAT INCLUDED ALLIES LIKE **REV. WILL CAMPBELL.**

LOOK, THE VIOLENCE **IS** GOING TO GET WORSE AND WORSE UNTIL SOMEONE IS KILLED--

HOW CAN IT BE THE RIGHT THING TO DO, TO CONTINUE PUTTING YOUNG PEOPLE IN HARM'S WAY?

WHAT DO **YOU** THINK, JOHN?

BUT I HEARD NOTHING THAT NIGHT TO CHANGE MY MIND.

uh huh,

I RESPECTED CAMPBELL AND THOSE WHO SHARED HIS CONCERNS,

We're gonna MARCH.

--AND WHAT DO YOU THINK WE SHOULD DO ABOUT THE **POLICE**, WHO ARE JUST AS DANGEROUS AS SOME OF THE OTHERS?

We're gonna MARCH.

JOHN! YOU'RE AGREEING WITH EVERYTHING EVERYONE IN THIS ROOM IS SAYING, BUT ALL YOU SAY IS, "WE'RE GONNA MARCH." THERE'S APT TO BE SOME VERY SERIOUS VIOLENCE IF WE HAVE ANOTHER DEMONSTRATION.

YOU AGREE WITH THAT, AND STILL YOU SAY, "WE'RE GONNA MARCH."

WHAT IT COMES DOWN TO IS THAT THIS IS JUST A MATTER OF PRIDE TO YOU. THIS IS ABOUT YOUR OWN STUBBORNNESS.

YOUR OWN SIN.

then i'm a SINNER.

but we're gonna MARCH.

SO THE NEXT EVENING, I LED THE PROTESTS.

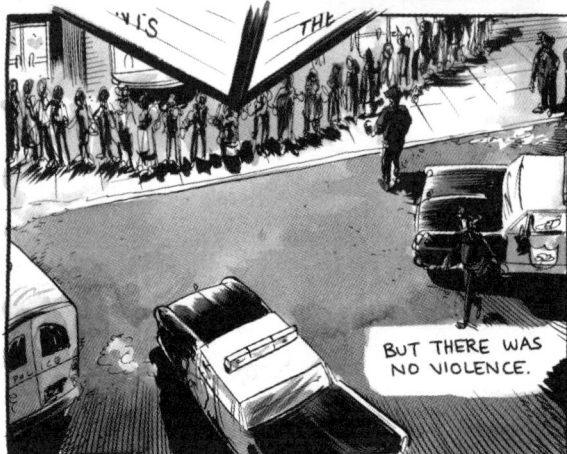

KLIK

NOW SHOWING
CECIL B DEMILLE'S
THE TEN COMMANDMENTS

BUT THERE WAS NO VIOLENCE.

TWENTY-SIX OF US WERE ARRESTED.

EVEN THOUGH I WAS SUPPOSED TO GIVE MY SENIOR SERMON THE NEXT DAY,

You know the drill-- whites to the left, coloreds over here!

ICE

WE REFUSED TO POST BAIL.

SO I SPENT FEBRUARY 21, 1961--
MY TWENTY-FIRST BIRTHDAY--
IN JAIL.

U.S. CAPITOL -- 10:21 AM, JANUARY 20, 2009

NOW ENTERING
MURFREESBORO
TENNESSEE

almost
there!

LEWIS, YOU
BE CAREFUL.

I KNOW YOU'RE STARTING
THIS JOURNEY IN WASHINGTON,
BUT AFTER YOU GET GOING,
WELL-- THESE PLACES ARE
NOT LIKE NASHVILLE.

YOU'RE HEADED INTO
THE **DEEP** SOUTH--
THE HEART OF THE BEAST.

JOHN, I LOVE
YOU, BROTHER--
KEEP YOUR **EYES**
ON THE **PRIZE.**

I'LL SEE YOU AGAIN
IN A FEW WEEKS,
BERNARD.

I KNOW. BUT
THIS IS SOMETHING
I **HAVE** TO **DO.**

one way or
another.

IN LATE MARCH 1961, A
FRIEND SHOWED ME AN
AD IN **THE STUDENT
VOICE,** A MONTHLY
SNCC PUBLICATION.

IT ANNOUNCED THAT THE **CONGRESS OF RACIAL EQUALITY** (CORE) WAS SEEKING VOLUNTEERS TO TEST THE SUPREME COURT DECISION FROM THE PREVIOUS YEAR, **BOYNTON V. VIRGINIA**,

DC, huh? okay, back of the bus.

WHICH OUTLAWED SEGREGATION AND RACIAL DISCRIMINATION ON BUSES AND IN BUS TERMINALS.

ITS TITLE WAS SIMPLE.

FREEDOM RIDE 1961

ACTUALLY, BERNARD AND I HAD WRITTEN A LETTER EARLIER THAT YEAR TO REV. **FRED SHUTTLESWORTH**, TALKING ABOUT AN IDEA WE HAD FOR A SMALL GROUP OF INTEGRATED STUDENTS TO RIDE BUSES INTO BIRMINGHAM TO TEST THE **BOYNTON** DECISION.

HE WROTE US BACK, BUT SAID HE THOUGHT IT WAS TOO DANGEROUS, AND THE SITUATION IN BIRMINGHAM TOO **VOLATILE**.

YOU ARE NOW LEAVING Tennessee

SO WHEN I SAW THAT AD, I FELT IT WAS THE **SPIRIT OF HISTORY** AT WORK AGAIN.

ON MY APPLICATION, I WROTE: "I KNOW THAT AN EDUCATION IS IMPORTANT AND I HOPE TO GET ONE, BUT HUMAN **DIGNITY** IS THE MOST IMPORTANT THING IN MY LIFE.

"THIS IS THE MOST IMPORTANT DECISION IN MY LIFE — TO DECIDE TO GIVE UP **ALL** IF NECESSARY FOR THE FREEDOM RIDE, THAT JUSTICE AND FREEDOM MIGHT COME TO THE DEEP SOUTH."

THEY LET ME IN.

APRIL 30, 1961.

LOOKING OUT AT **WASHINGTON, DC** FOR THE FIRST TIME IN MY LIFE WAS **MAGICAL.**

GREYHOUND

I HEADED TO **THE FELLOWSHIP HOUSE,** WHICH WAS RUN BY QUAKERS AS A SORT OF HEADQUARTERS FOR PACIFIST ORGANIZATIONS.

NOK NOK

KLIK

JOHN, WELCOME--

I'M JAMES FARMER.

PLEASE, COME MEET EVERYONE--

YOU'RE THE LAST TO ARRIVE.

THIS CORE INITIATIVE WILL BE HISTORIC, AND AS THE EXECUTIVE DIRECTOR OF CORE, I'M HAPPY TO HAVE YOU BE A PART OF IT.

WELL THEN-- LET ME INTRODUCE YOU TO YOUR FELLOW FREEDOM RIDERS.

THERE WAS JOE PERKINS, A KENTUCKY NATIVE WHO LEFT GRADUATE SCHOOL TO BECOME A CORE FIELD SECRETARY.

JIM PECK--HE HAD BEEN ON CORE'S FIRST FREEDOM RIDE, THE JOURNEY OF RECONCILIATION IN 1947, WHICH LANDED ALL ITS PARTICIPANTS IN A CHAIN GANG.

ELTON COX--A MINISTER FROM NORTH CAROLINA.

DR. WALTER BERGMAN, A PROFESSOR FROM THE UNIVERSITY OF MICHIGAN, AND HIS WIFE FRANCES.

THERE WAS JIMMY McDONALD-- A PLAYFUL GUY, HE WAS A FOLK SINGER FROM NEW YORK.

18-YEAR-OLD CHARLES PERSON, A PHYSICS STUDENT FROM MOREHOUSE COLLEGE.

ED BLANKENHEIM-- CORE STAFF MEMBER.

GENEVIEVE HUGHES-- A CORE FIELD SECRETARY.

THERE WAS ALBERT BIGELOW-- A PACIFIST ARRESTED IN 1958 FOR STEERING A SKIFF CALLED THE GOLDEN RULE INTO A NUCLEAR TESTING ZONE IN THE SOUTH PACIFIC, PROTESTING THE USE OF ATOMIC WEAPONS.

HANK THOMAS -- A HOWARD UNIVERSITY SENIOR.

AND JAMES FARMER-- THE LEADER OF OUR GROUP.

TOGETHER, WE SPENT THE NEXT THREE DAYS TRAINING, PREPARING OURSELVES FOR WHAT LAY AHEAD.

WE BEGAN BY COVERING MUCH OF WHAT I HAD SPENT YEARS LEARNING FROM JIM LAWSON-- **GANDHI, THOREAU, EMERSON...**

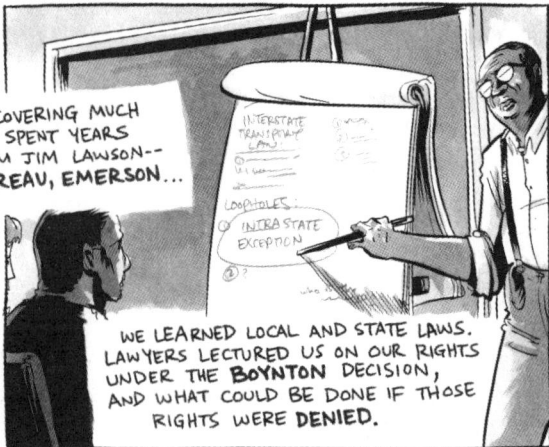

INTERSTATE TRANSPORT LAW

LOOPHOLES:
INTRA STATE EXCEPTION

WE LEARNED LOCAL AND STATE LAWS. LAWYERS LECTURED US ON OUR RIGHTS UNDER THE **BOYNTON** DECISION, AND WHAT COULD BE DONE IF THOSE RIGHTS WERE **DENIED.**

THERE WAS VERY LITTLE DOWNTIME, BUT ONCE OR TWICE JIMMY MCDONALD PICKED UP HIS GUITAR AND SANG.

which side are you on, boy--? ♪♪ which side are you on? ♪

ON THE NIGHT BEFORE WE STARTED OUR JOURNEY, WE WENT OUT TO EAT AT A NICE CHINESE RESTAURANT.

I HAD NEVER ACTUALLY EATEN AT A RESTAURANT BEFORE IN MY LIFE--

THE ONLY OTHER TIMES I HAD STEPPED FOOT INSIDE ONE HAD BEEN PART OF A **PROTEST.**

CLINK CLINK

≡ ahem ≡

IF I COULD GET YOUR ATTENTION, PLEASE--

RIDERS--

I HAVE FAITH IN YOUR ABILITY TO MEET **ANY** CHALLENGE, BUT I ALSO WANT YOU TO KNOW THAT I'M **THE ONLY** PERSON OBLIGATED TO GO ON THIS TRIP.

YOU ARE FREE TO CHOOSE WHETHER TO JOIN ME--AND IF YOU CHOOSE **NOT** TO GO, THERE WILL BE NO BLAME, NO RECRIMINATION, AND **CORE** WILL PAY FOR YOUR TRAVELS BACK HOME.

EAT WELL, EVERYONE--

THIS MAY BE OUR LAST SUPPER.

WE ALL KNEW WHAT HE SAID WAS TRUE--

THE **WILLS** WE'D SIGNED THAT WEEK SERVED AS TESTAMENT.

shuffle

MAY 4, 1961 -- TRAILWAYS BUS STATION, WASHINGTON, DC.

DEPA

PHILADELPHIA......8:31
NEW YORK.........8:52
TRENTON..........9:40
RICHMOND.........9:53
CINCINNATI.......10:12
PITTSBURGH.......11:24
ROANOKE..........11:51

ARRIVALS

ONE-WAY TICKET, PLEASE.

WHERE YOU GOING?

NEW ORLEANS.

MR. FARMER-- WHAT ARE THE RIDERS' STRATEGIES TO DEAL WITH ANY POTENTIAL HOSTILITIES ON THIS JOURNEY?

IF THERE IS AN ARREST, WE WILL **ACCEPT** THAT ARREST, AND IF THERE IS VIOLENCE WE WILL **ACCEPT** THAT VIOLENCE WITHOUT RESPONDING IN KIND.

WE WILL **NOT** PAY FINES BECAUSE WE FEEL THAT, BY PAYING MONEY TO A SEGREGATED STATE, WE WOULD HELP IT PERPETUATE SEGREGATION.

NEXT QUESTION, PLEASE--

YOU, SIR?

WE SPLIT INTO TWO GROUPS.

MY SEATMATE WAS ALBERT BIGELOW.

IN ACCORDANCE WITH GANDHIAN PRINCIPLES, BEFORE WE LEFT FARMER SENT OUT A LETTER WITH THE PLANS FOR OUR ACT OF **CIVIL DISOBEDIENCE**--

HE MAILED COPIES TO PRESIDENT KENNEDY,
ATTORNEY GENERAL ROBERT F. KENNEDY,
FBI DIRECTOR J. EDGAR HOOVER, TO THE
CHAIRMAN OF THE INTERSTATE COMMERCE
COMMISSION, AND TO THE PRESIDENTS OF BOTH
GREYHOUND AND TRAILWAYS BUS COMPANIES.

THOSE LETTERS WERE
NEVER ANSWERED.

OUR FIRST STOP WAS FREDERICKSBURG.

LOOKS LIKE THEY KNEW WE WERE COMING AND BAKED US A CAKE.

MEN

MEN

IT WAS THE SAME IN RICHMOND AND PETERSBURG, WHERE WE STAYED THE NIGHT.

WE LEFT THE NEXT MORNING FOR FARMVILLE, THEN ON TO LYNCHBURG AND DANVILLE.

IN CHARLOTTE, JOE PERKINS ASKED FOR A SHOESHINE IN A BARBER SHOP, AND WAS PROMPTLY ARRESTED FOR TRESPASSING.

JOE'S CHARGE WAS THROWN OUT THE NEXT DAY, BUT BY THEN WE WERE IN ROCK HILL, SOUTH CAROLINA.

I COULD TELL WE WERE IN TROUBLE AS SOON AS I STEPPED OFF THE BUS.

WHITES

other side, nigger.

I HAVE A RIGHT TO GO IN HERE, ON THE GROUNDS OF THE SUPREME COURT DECISION IN THE **BOYNTON** CASE--

SHIT ON THAT.

KRAK

DO YOU WISH TO PRESS CHARGES?

AND YOU?

NO, SIR.

NO, SIR.

THAT NIGHT WE STAYED AT FRIENDSHIP JUNIOR COLLEGE, AND ALMOST AS SOON AS I GOT THERE,

I RECEIVED A TELEGRAM.

EXCUSE ME, JOHN LEWIS?

IT WAS FROM THE AMERICAN FRIENDS SERVICE COMMITTEE-- THE QUAKERS. THEY'D TRACKED ME DOWN THROUGH NASHVILLE--

THEY WERE INVITING ME TO COME TO PHILADELPHIA FOR A PHYSICAL, AND TO COMPLETE MY INTERVIEW FOR A TWO-YEAR VOLUNTEER PROGRAM IN INDIA THAT WAS VERY SIMILAR TO THE PEACE CORPS.

IT WAS A TOUGH DECISION--
I'D OFTEN IMAGINED LIVING ABROAD.

SO I DECIDED TO GO
TO PHILADELPHIA.

IF ALL WENT AS PLANNED, I'D
TAKE A FLIGHT BACK TO NASHVILLE
AFTER MY INTERVIEW, AND THEN
TAKE A CAR TO BIRMINGHAM ON
SUNDAY, MAY 14th-- MOTHER'S DAY--
TO **REJOIN** THE FREEDOM RIDERS.

BUT MY GROUP NEVER MADE IT
TO BIRMINGHAM.

MAY 14, 1961 --
NASHVILLE, TENNESSEE.

WHEN I GOT BACK TO NASHVILLE, I ATTENDED A PICNIC TO CELEBRATE THE FACT THAT, AFTER **FOURTEEN WEEKS** OF STAND-INS, THE CITY'S THEATER OWNERS HAD FINALLY AGREED TO **DESEGREGATE.**

WE WENT BACK AND WE WENT BACK. FORTY TIMES WE DEMONSTRATED AT THOSE THEATERS!

JUST LIKE THE BIBLE'S GREAT FLOOD, FORTY DAYS AND FORTY NIGHTS WE--

♪--WE HAVE A **BREAKING NEWS BULLETIN**--

AFTERWARDS, I WOULD SET OFF TO REJOIN THE FREEDOM RIDES--

AT LEAST, THAT WAS THE **PLAN.**

--AT THIS TIME, A **GREYHOUND BUS** CARRYING FREEDOM RIDERS IS REPORTED TO BE **IN FLAMES** OUTSIDE OF ANNISTON, ALABAMA--

THAT'S **MY BUS**!!

REPORTS INDICATE THAT THE BUS WAS **FIREBOMBED**-- WE HAVE NO WORD YET ON CASUALTIES OR INJURIES BUT DETAILS WILL BE FORTHCOMING. OUR SOURCES CLAIM TO

OH MY GOD!

WE'VE GOT TO DO SOMET-

WHAT!!

COME ON, LET'S GO!

HURRY, HURRY! MORE REPORTS ARE STARTING TO COME IN!

WE RACED TO MEET UP AT FIRST BAPTIST.

DDRRRRRR

HELLO?
HELLO?!

CAN YOU HEAR ME?!

ONE WITNESS DE SEEING WINDOW AND TIRES SL BEFORE AN EXPLO

...yes?

THIS IS DIANE NASH-- I'M CALLING FOR JAMES FARMER.

KLIK

wh--

HE'S IN WASHINGTON?!

okay--

AT THIS TIME, IS NOT KNOWN THE ASSAILA BE CON

HELLO?! IS JAMES FARMER IN?

well, DO YOU KNOW WHERE HE IS?!

I'M CALLING FROM NASHVILLE.

ALLEYS AND CORRIDORS,

POUNDING THEM WITH PIPES, WITH KEY RINGS, AND WITH FISTS.

...TOUGH! GRABBED THE PASSENGERS INTO ALLEYS AND CORRIDORS

TURN IT UP!!

yeah, and we do that first, then the locals.

hey--

okay, you get in touch with everyone on that list from no/from st dept, and i'll take...

HEY!

ONE PASSENGER WAS KNOCKED DOWN AT MY FEET BY TWELVE HOODLUMS, AND HIS FACE WAS BEATEN INTO A BLOODY RED PULP.

HEY!!

THE SECOND BUS MADE IT TO BIRMINGHAM, BUT THEY GOT THAT ONE, TOO.

CLICK!

hummmmmmm

--CHIEF CONNOR, AFTER THE EVENTS IN ANNISTON, WHERE A BUS CARRYING FREEDOM RIDERS WAS ATTACKED BY A MOB AND FIREBOMBED--

--CAN YOU TELL US WHY THERE WERE NO POLICE OFFICERS PRESENT AT THE BIRMINGHAM BUS STATION WHEN THE SECOND BUS FINALLY DID ARRIVE?

EUGENE "BULL" CONNOR-- HE WAS BIRMINGHAM'S CHIEF OF POLICE. EVERYONE WAS AFRAID OF HIM--

EVEN THE GOVERNOR.

MOTHER'S DAY.

WE TRY AND LET OFF AS MANY OF OUR POLICEMEN AS POSSIBLE, SO THEY CAN SPEND MOTHER'S DAY AT HOME WITH THEIR FAMILIES.

WE FOUND OUT LATER THAT HE'D PROMISED THE KU KLUX KLAN FIFTEEN MINUTES WITH THE BUS BEFORE HE'D MAKE ANY ARRESTS.

WORD CAME THE NEXT DAY THAT JAMES FARMER WAS **CALLING OFF** THE RIDES.

hello--?

can I speak to James Farmer, please?

MR. FARMER? THIS IS DIANE NASH.

I COULDN'T BELIEVE IT. WE COULD **NOT** JUST GIVE UP.

I'M SORRY--

WHO IS THIS?

DIANE NASH--

ATTORNEY GENERAL **ROBERT KENNEDY** WAS BECOMING MORE AND MORE INVOLVED IN THE FEDERAL GOVERNMENT'S RESPONSE. HIS AIDE, **JOHN SEIGENTHALER**, HAD ARRANGED AN AIRPLANE TO FLY THE REMAINING FREEDOM RIDERS OUT OF ALABAMA.

-- I'M WITH THE NASHVILLE STUDENT MOVEMENT.

MR. FARMER, WE WANT TO **RESUME** THE FREEDOM RIDE.

I'M CALLING TO ASK FOR YOUR SUPPORT.

YOU...

... YOU REALIZE IT MAY BE SUICIDE?

YOU COULD BE MASSACRED.

49

THE PRESIDENT-ELECT OF THE UNITED STATES, BARACK H. OBAMA!

congratulations, Mr. President.

thank you, John.

I'll need your prayers.

you'll have them.

WEDNESDAY, MAY 17, 1961--
BIRMINGHAM CITY LIMITS.

TEN OF US SET OUT FROM NASHVILLE TO TAKE THE PLACE OF THE BLOODIED RIDERS WHOSE BUSES WERE ATTACKED IN ANNISTON AND BIRMINGHAM, AND TO PICK UP WHERE THEY LEFT OFF.

BUT THE **POLICE** CAUGHT UP TO US BEFORE WE MADE IT ALL THE WAY INTO TOWN.

YOU TWO--

STAND UP!

YOU'RE UNDER ARREST FOR VIOLATING STATE LAW--

YOU **KNOW** WHITE PEOPLE AND NIGGERS CAN'T SIT TOGETHER!

JIM ZWERG AND **PAUL BROOKS** WERE TAKEN TO JAIL ALMOST IMMEDIATELY.

WE WERE ALL ON EDGE, KNOWING WHAT THIS CITY HAD DONE TO THE **OTHER** RIDERS.

EVERYONE ELSE--

PLEASE PRODUCE YOUR TICKETS.

DR. BERGMAN, STILL BLOODY FROM THE FIRST BUS'S ATTACK IN ANNISTON, WAS BRUTALLY BEATEN AGAIN ON THE TERMINAL FLOOR IN BIRMINGHAM.

HE SUSTAINED PERMANENT BRAIN DAMAGE AND A STROKE THAT WOULD **PARALYZE** HIM FOR THE REST OF HIS LIFE.

=ahem=

FELLOW RIDER **SALYNN McCOLLUM**, WHO HAD A DIFFERENT TICKET, SLIPPED OUT TO CALL **DIANE NASH** AND ALERT HER OF THE SITUATION.

THREE HOURS LATER.

KL-INK

SQUEEEEEEEE

COME ON.

FRED! SALYNN!

LET'S GET YOU ALL **OUT** OF THAT MESS FOR NOW.

KLOP

KLOP

KLOP
KLOP

YOU ARE ALL
UNDER ARREST.

BOYS.

... FOR YOUR OWN
PROTECTION.

NOW, HOLD ON
A MINUTE--

TAKE MISTER
SHUTTLESWORTH
HERE, TOO.

11:30 PM,
THURSDAY
MAY 18, 1961.

CL-CLANK

CL-CLANK

AND JUST TO MAKE SURE YOU GET THERE--

I'M PUTTING YOU PEOPLE UNDER PROTECTIVE CUSTODY, AND SENDING YOU ALL THE WAY BACK TO NASHVILLE WHERE YOU BELONG.

--I'M GONNA RIDE ALONG.

MR. CONNOR--

WHEN WE GET TO NASHVILLE, YOU'RE WELCOME TO JOIN US FOR BREAKFAST AT THE FISK CAFETERIA.

IT WOULD BE MY PLEASURE.

VR-- VRMMMM

THIS IS WHERE YOU'LL BE GETTIN' OUT.

THERE'S THE TENNESSEE LINE--

CROSS IT, AND SAVE THIS STATE AND YOURSELF A LOTTA TROUBLE.

WHUMP

WRRMMMRRMMMMM

Y'ALL CAN CATCH A TRAIN FROM HERE.

OR MAYBE A BUS!

HAR!

WELCOME TO Alabama

SCRREEEEE

THEY WERE BRAVE AND COURAGEOUS PEOPLE TO TAKE US ALL IN.

LUCKILY, THEY HAD A TELEPHONE, AND WE WERE ABLE TO TELL DIANE IN NASHVILLE ABOUT WHAT HAD HAPPENED.

I'LL HAVE A CAR ON ITS WAY TO YOU.

ELEVEN OTHER "PACKAGES" HAVE BEEN SHIPPED DOWN TO BIRMINGHAM...

...JOHN, WHERE DO I SEND THE REST OF THE PACKAGES?

SEND THEM TO BIRMINGHAM, TOO.

SEND THEM ALL TO BIRMINGHAM.

WHEN DAYBREAK CAME, WE TOLD THIS KIND COUPLE THAT WE HADN'T HAD ANYTHING TO EAT, AND WE GAVE THEM SOME MONEY.

WE WERE SO HUNGRY--

BUT NOT FOR LONG.

A YOUNG GUY BY THE NAME OF LEO LILLARD DROVE HIS CAR ALL THE WAY FROM NASHVILLE TO PICK US UP.

seriously, how are we supposed to FIT?!

somehow.

WE STARTED DOWN THE HIGHWAY AND HEARD A NEWS BULLETIN!

THIS JUST IN--THE FREEDOM RIDERS ARE BACK IN NASHVILLE, AND HAVE RETURNED TO THEIR COLLEGE CAMPUSES...

WE WERE ECSTATIC THAT THEY DIDN'T KNOW WHERE WE WERE--

BUT THE MOOD QUICKLY FADED.

THEY-- WE ARE NOW REPORTING THAT THE STUDENTS ARE ON THEIR WAY TO BIRMINGHAM IN A PRIVATE CAR.

wha--!

hang on, everybody--

THEY KNEW WE WERE COMING.

time for a DETOUR!

WELCOME TO BIRMINGHAM

SOMEHOW, WE MADE IT BACK UNDETECTED THROUGH LESS-TRAVELED ROADS.

WE ALL HAD A MEAL TOGETHER BEFORE BEING DRIVEN DOWN TO THE GREYHOUND STATION TO RESUME THE FREEDOM RIDES.

66

FINALLY, WE WERE ALLOWED TO GO INTO THE SO-CALLED WHITE WAITING ROOM, WHERE WE STAYED THE ENTIRE EVENING.

WE WERE HEARING A **LOT** OF THINGS AT THE TIME, BUT DIDN'T KNOW WHAT TO BELIEVE.

--AND WE HEARD THAT BOBBY KENNEDY SAID, "THE PEOPLE HAVE A RIGHT TO TRAVEL"--

but he wants all of you OUT of Birmingham.

He thinks Birmingham is too dangerous.

ALL I KNEW WAS THAT ATTORNEY GENERAL ROBERT KENNEDY COULD NOT COUNT ON **ANY** COOPERATION FROM STATE OR LOCAL AUTHORITIES.

WE HEARD THAT ROBERT KENNEDY AND HIS AIDE, **JOHN SEIGENTHALER**, HAD BEEN TALKING TO GOVERNOR **JOHN PATTERSON** AS WELL AS GREYHOUND OFFICIALS TO WORK OUT A SOLUTION.

WE COULDN'T SLEEP, AND THERE WAS NOTHING TO EAT--

BUT THAT NIGHT, WE HAD MORE SERIOUS CONCERNS.

KLAK KLAK KLAK KLAK KLAK KLAK

WE HAVE A BUS READY.

I know, and I don't care.

I know.

Joe, please.

I'M SUPPOSED TO DRIVE THIS BUS TO DOTHAN, ALABAMA, THROUGH MONTGOMERY, BUT I UNDERSTAND THERE'S A BIG CONVOY DOWN THE ROAD.

I ONLY HAVE ONE LIFE TO GIVE, AND I'M **NOT** GOING TO GIVE IT TO **CORE** OR THE NAACP.

IT MAY SOUND STRANGE, BUT AT THE TIME I WAS MORE SHOCKED THAT THIS WHITE BUS DRIVER KNEW ENOUGH ABOUT US TO REFERENCE **CORE** BY NAME.

PEOPLE WERE STARTING TO NOTICE US, EVEN IF WE DIDN'T CHANGE THEIR MINDS.

EVERYTHING WAS UP IN THE AIR UNTIL BULL CONNOR SHOWED UP TO TALK TO THE DRIVER, ALONG WITH GREYHOUND OFFICIALS AND LEADERS FROM THE LOCAL BUS DRIVERS' UNION.

FINALLY, AT 8:30 IN THE MORNING ON MAY 20, 1961, WE RESUMED THE FREEDOM RIDES.

I-65 SOUTHBOUND, 5 MILES OUTSIDE
MONTGOMERY, AL--
9:55 AM, MAY 20, 1961.

SQUEEE

this doesn't look right.

PSSHHK

MISTER LEWIS--

WHAMM

CRUNCH
CRUNCH

WHAP!

KRUNCH!

nigger lover!

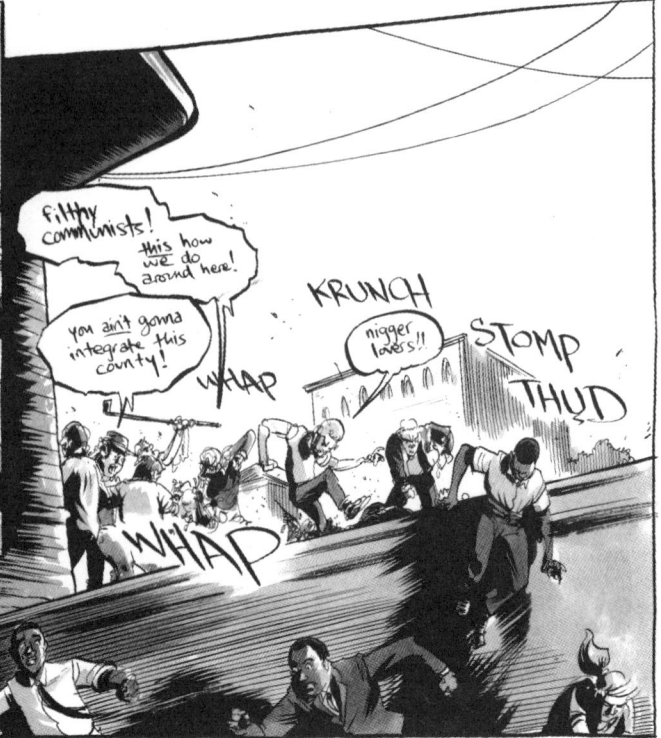

filthy communists!

this how we do around here!

you ain't gonna integrate this county!

WHAP

KRUNCH

nigger lovers!!

STOMP
THUD

WHAP

KRAK

VRRRMMMM

ERT!!

HEY!

WHUMP

MISTER, THIS IS **NOT** YOUR FIGHT-- GET AWAY FROM HERE!! YOU'RE GONNA GET KILLED!!

WAIT--!

LADY, GET YOUR BUTT IN THE--

WHO THE HELL ARE YOU?!

MY NAME'S JOHN SEIGENTHALER-- I'M A FEDERAL AGENT.

I'M HERE ON DIRECT ORDERS FROM THE--

SPLAT

IT WAS **FLOYD MANN**, ALABAMA'S PUBLIC SAFETY DIRECTOR, WHO SAVED OUR LIVES.

I'LL SHOOT THE NEXT MAN THAT HITS HIM.

THERE'LL BE NO KILLING HERE TODAY.

♪ ♫ Y' COUNTRY, 'TIS OF THEE, ♪ ♫

FIRST BAPTIST CHURCH--
MONTGOMERY, AL-- 8:08 PM, MAY 21, 1961

BOOM!

AFTER HEARING OF THE VIOLENCE AT THE
BUS STATION, DR. MARTIN LUTHER KING, JR.
FLEW TO MONTGOMERY.

A MASS MEETING WAS CALLED
AT RALPH ABERNATHY'S CHURCH.
GOVERNOR PATTERSON, DESPITE PROMISING
TO PROTECT US, HAD WARRANTS SWORN
OUT FOR OUR ARREST. WE RIDERS
DECIDED TO SCATTER OURSELVES
THROUGHOUT THE CHURCH'S PEWS IN
CASE THE POLICE TRIED TO ARREST US.

all right!

yeah!!

BOOM!

BURN IT!

so now...
let's clean these
niggers outta
here!

CREAK
FBOOM!

BY SUNSET, MORE THAN 1,500 PEOPLE HAD PACKED THE CHURCH.

JUST AS THE CROWD INSIDE THE CHURCH
GREW, SO DID THE CROWD OF WHITES
OUTSIDE. AND THEY WERE ANGRY.

THE MEETING DIDN'T BEGIN UNTIL FRED SHUTTLESWORTH ARRIVED SAFELY WITH JAMES FARMER.

DR. KING INTRODUCED FARMER TO THE CONGREGATION, AND BROUGHT HIM UP TO THE PULPIT.

THEN THEY ASKED ME TO COME UP AS WELL.

THE TWO REMAINING ORIGINAL FREEDOM RIDERS -- REUNITED.

TINK!

CRASH!

SMASH!

T-TINK TINK

AS THE MEETING CONTINUED, WE POURED OUR HEARTS INTO THE MUSIC OF THE MOVEMENT, SONGS LIKE "AIN'T NOBODY GONNA TURN ME 'ROUND" AND "WE SHALL OVERCOME", TO GIVE US STRENGTH.

CRASH!

MEANWHILE, AS I SOON LEARNED, DR. KING HEADED TO THE OFFICE FOR A PHONE CALL WITH ROBERT KENNEDY.

I WAS ASKED TO JOIN JAMES FARMER AND DIANE NASH AS DR. KING EXPLAINED ROBERT KENNEDY'S REQUEST.

I WON'T STOP IT NOW. IF I DO, WE'LL JUST GET WORDS AND PROMISES.

IT IS NOT WITHOUT MERIT TO SAY THAT THE FREEDOM RIDE HAS ALREADY MADE ITS POINT, AND NOW SHOULD BE CALLED OFF.

NO.

THE NASHVILLE STUDENT MOVEMENT WANTS TO GO ON. WE CAN'T STOP IT NOW, RIGHT AFTER WE'VE BEEN CLOBBERED!

PLEASE TELL THE ATTORNEY GENERAL THAT WE'VE BEEN COOLING OFF FOR 350 YEARS--

IF WE COOL OFF ANY MORE, WE WILL BE IN A DEEP FREEZE.

THE FREEDOM RIDE WILL GO ON.

VERY WELL.

I'LL TELL HIM.

A FEW U.S. MARSHALS HAD ARRIVED,
BUT THEY STRUGGLED OUTSIDE TO HOLD THE MOB BACK...

...AND IT QUICKLY BEGAN TO LOOK LIKE THEY WOULD BE **OVERWHELMED.**

UNEXPECTEDLY, THE ALABAMA NATIONAL GUARD ARRIVED AND SENT THE MARSHALS AWAY.

AFTER HOURS OF REFUSING TO SPEAK WITH ANY FEDERAL OFFICIAL, GOVERNOR PATTERSON HAD FINALLY ORDERED MONTGOMERY TO BE PUT UNDER WHAT HE CALLED "QUALIFIED MARTIAL LAW."

AND SO, WE CONTINUED OUR MEETING.

WYATT WALKER SPOKE, FOLLOWED BY RALPH ABERNATHY, AND THEN JAMES FARMER. BUT DR. KING BROUGHT IT HOME.

GOVERNOR PATTERSON BEARS THE ULTIMATE RESPONSIBILITY FOR THE HIDEOUS ACTION IN ALABAMA.

HIS CONSISTENT PREACHING OF DEFIANCE OF THE LAW, HIS VITRIOLIC PUBLIC PRONOUNCEMENTS, AND HIS IRRESPONSIBLE ACTIONS HAVE CREATED THE ATMOSPHERE IN WHICH VIOLENCE COULD THRIVE.

THEN FRED SHUTTLESWORTH SPOKE, AND MADE IT QUITE PLAIN.

IT'S A SIN AND A SHAME BEFORE GOD THAT THESE PEOPLE WHO GOVERN US WOULD LET THINGS COME TO SUCH A SAD STATE. BUT GOD IS NOT DEAD.

THE MOST GUILTY MAN IN THIS STATE TONIGHT IS GOVERNOR PATTERSON.

FINALLY, JUST AFTER MIDNIGHT, THE MEETING FINISHED.

WE STARTED TO LEAVE,

ONLY TO FIND THAT THOSE SAME TROOPS SUPPOSEDLY SENT TO PROTECT US, NOW **HELD** US INSIDE THE CHURCH.

OUT OF THE WAY--

ALL RIGHT, BACK UP, BACK UP!

GENERAL HENRY GRAHAM OF THE ALABAMA NATIONAL GUARD,

A REAL ESTATE AGENT IN HIS CIVILIAN LIFE,

REFUSED TO ALLOW ANYONE TO LEAVE.

KLOP

KLOP

STOMP

: ahem :

"WHEREAS, AS A RESULT OF OUTSIDE AGITATORS COMING INTO ALABAMA TO VIOLATE OUR LAWS AND CUSTOMS...

THEY KEPT US IN THE CHURCH ALMOST ALL NIGHT.

FINALLY, AROUND 4:30 IN THE MORNING, WE WERE ALLOWED TO LEAVE.

THE NEXT DAY, A JUDGE **LIFTED** THE INJUNCTION AGAINST THE FREEDOM RIDERS. WE MET THAT EVENING TO ORGANIZE THE CONTINUATION OF THE RIDES.

JAMES FARMER WAS TALKING A LOT, TRYING TO TAKE CONTROL. BUT IT RUBBED A LOT OF PEOPLE THE WRONG WAY.

ANOTHER ISSUE WAS DR. KING'S PARTICIPATION IN THE RIDES.

MARTIN, ARE YOU GOING TO JOIN US? WILL YOU RIDE WITH US?

I CAN'T GO, DIANE.

I'M STILL ON PROBATION FROM MY ARREST IN ATLANTA.

I'm on probation, too!

Me too!

Same here.

yeah

WE'RE ALL ON PROBATION, DR. KING.

... I think I should choose the time and place of my GOLGOTHA.

tsk!

de LAWD!

MONTGOMERY, AL--
MAY 23, 1961.

I'M GOING TO READ A STATEMENT.

THE NEXT DAY WE HELD A PRESS CONFERENCE ANNOUNCING OUR INTENTION TO CONTINUE THE FREEDOM RIDES TO JACKSON, MISSISSIPPI-- THE HEART OF THE BEAST.

FPASH!

FLASH!

THE FREEDOM RIDERS WILL SOON BOARD BUSES FOR MISSISSIPPI, WITH OR WITHOUT GUARANTEES OF POLICE PROTECTION.

BEFORE LEAVING, THEY WILL PARTICIPATE IN A NONVIOLENT WORKSHOP LED BY REVEREND JIM LAWSON.

FREEDOM RIDERS MUST DEVELOP THE QUIET COURAGE OF DYING FOR A CAUSE.

WE ALL LOVE LIFE, AND THERE ARE NO MARTYRS HERE-- BUT WE ARE WELL AWARE THAT WE MAY HAVE SOME CASUALTIES.

I'M SURE THESE STUDENTS ARE WILLING TO FACE DEATH IF NECESSARY.

ERT!

EARLY THE NEXT MORNING, WE WERE DRIVEN TO THE BUS STATION BY NATIONAL GUARD TROOPS, FOR OUR OWN PROTECTION.

? hey JIM!

JIM FARMER--!

YOU'RE GOING WITH US, AREN'T YOU?

yeah, Jim!

yeahhh, uh gee, well uh you know i've got a lot of paperwork is the thing, and you know CoRE really needs somebody to run...

Come on!

JIM, PLEASE!

all right!

yeah Jim!

JACKSON, MS-- MAY 24, 1961

WHEN WE GOT TO THE JACKSON BUS STATION, WE LEARNED THAT EVERYONE FROM THE BUS AHEAD OF US HAD ALREADY BEEN TAKEN TO JAIL.

WHITE WAITING

COLORED WAITING

BUT THAT DIDN'T STOP US.

WHITES ONLY

WHITE MEN'S RESTROOM

AFTER OUR ARRESTS IN JACKSON, ROBERT KENNEDY WAS QUICKLY LOSING PATIENCE WITH US.

THEY MUST USE THEIR LIVES AND BODIES TO RIGHT A WRONG.

MR. ATTORNEY GENERAL, IT'S A MATTER OF CONSCIENCE AND MORALITY--

OUR CONSCIENCE TELLS US THAT THE LAW IS WRONG, AND WE MUST RESIST-- BUT WE HAVE A MORAL OBLIGATION TO ACCEPT THE PENALTY.

WHEN HE FOUND OUT THAT ALL OF THE RIDERS HAD REFUSED TO POST BAIL, HE CALLED DR. KING TO SEE IF ANY OF US WOULD BE WILLING TO RECONSIDER.

Sigh

THAT IS NOT GOING TO HAVE THE SLIGHTEST EFFECT ON WHAT THE GOVERNMENT IS GOING TO DO IN THIS FIELD, OR ANY OTHER. THE FACT THAT THEY STAY IN JAIL IS NOT GOING TO HAVE THE SLIGHTEST EFFECT ON ME, DR. KING.

PERHAPS IT WOULD HELP IF THE STUDENTS CAME DOWN HERE BY THE HUNDREDS--

BY THE HUNDREDS OF THOUSANDS.

LOOK, THE COUNTRY BELONGS TO YOU AS MUCH AS TO ME. YOU DETERMINE WHAT'S BEST JUST AS WELL AS I CAN, BUT DON'T MAKE STATEMENTS THAT SOUND LIKE A THREAT.

THAT'S NOT THE WAY TO DEAL WITH US.

IT'S DIFFICULT TO UNDERSTAND THE POSITION OF OPPRESSED PEOPLE. OURS IS A WAY OUT-- CREATIVE, MORAL, AND NONVIOLENT.

IT IS NOT TIED TO BLACK SUPREMACY OR COMMUNISM, BUT TO THE PLIGHT OF THE OPPRESSED.

IT CAN SAVE THE SOUL OF AMERICA.

WHEN I ASK YOU A QUESTION, YOU FINISH YOUR ANSWERS WITH "SIR" BECAUSE I AM YOUR **SUPERIOR**.

DO YOU UNDERSTAND ME?!

INSTEAD, MUCH OF THE MEANS OF ENFORCING SEGREGATION CAME THROUGH ECONOMIC AND POLITICAL PRESSURE ORGANIZED BY A GROUP CALLED THE **WHITE CITIZENS' COUNCIL**.

BUT BEHIND CLOSED DOORS--

SORT OF LIKE A BUSINESSMAN'S KU KLUX KLAN.

YES.

GOD **DAMMIT!**

THE VIOLENCE COULD BE EVEN WORSE.

WE WERE QUICKLY TAKEN TO TRIAL. THE PROSECUTION ONLY CALLED ONE WITNESS, AND ALL **27** OF US WERE CONVICTED OF DISTURBING THE PEACE. WE WERE SENTENCED TO A $200 FINE EACH, AND A SUSPENDED SENTENCE OF **60 DAYS** IN JAIL.

REFUSING TO PAY THE FINE MEANT THAT WE WOULD **HAVE** TO SERVE OUR 60 DAYS IN JAIL. FOR MANY, THAT WAS A VERY FRIGHTENING PROSPECT.

BUT FOR ME, AND NEARLY EVERY OTHER FREEDOM RIDER, WE JUST WOULD **NOT** PAY THAT FINE.

AND SO WE WENT TO JAIL.

THREE DAYS AFTER OUR TRIAL, WE WERE TRANSFERRED TO HINDS COUNTY JAIL--

EVEN MORE CROWDED THAN JACKSON CITY HALL'S CELLS.

SOON, WORD MANAGED TO TRICKLE IN ABOUT WHAT WAS HAPPENING ON THE OUTSIDE.

IT ISN'T JUST A RIDE ANYMORE, JOHN--

THEY'RE HAPPENING ALL OVER, FOUR OR FIVE HERE, A DOZEN MORE THERE-- ALL GETTING ON BUSES TO JACKSON.

WE'LL SEE 'EM IN HERE WITH US BEFORE TOO LONG.

WITHIN TWO WEEKS OF OUR ARRIVAL IN HINDS COUNTY, THE GROWING NUMBER OF FREEDOM RIDERS BEING HOUSED WITHIN ITS WALLS FORCED THE LOCAL SHERIFF TO TRANSFER US TO ANOTHER PRISON...

MISSISSIPPI STATE PENITENTARY, AKA "PARCHMAN FARM"-- JUNE 15, 1961.

PARCHMAN WAS THE STUFF OF LEGENDS -- DARK LEGENDS.

21,000 ACRES OF BULLWHIP-WIELDING GUARDS AND HUMAN BONDAGE.

MISSISSIPPI STATE PENITENTARY

PROPERTY OF THE STATE OF MISSISSIPPI

THE SUPERINTENDENT HIMSELF, FRED JONES, GREETED US.

we have some bad niggers here.

we have niggers on death row that'll beat you up and cut you as soon as LOOK at you.

go ahead and sing your goddamn freedom songs now.

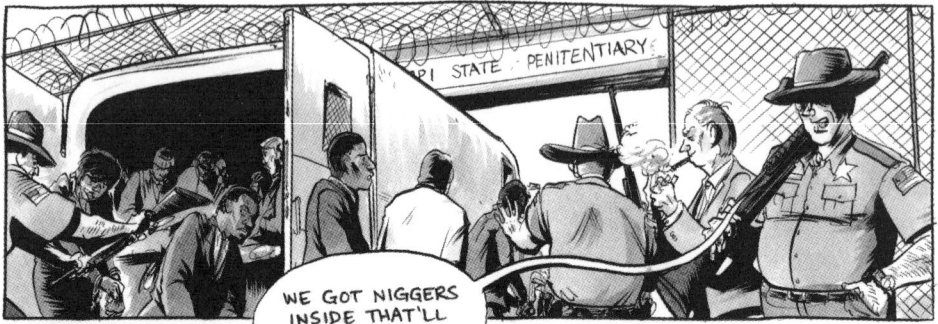

WE GOT NIGGERS INSIDE THAT'LL EAT YOU.

SO YOU GO AND SING YOUR SONGS INSIDE, NOW.

take off your shoes. then take off all your clothing.

IT WAS DEHUMANIZING,

SHOWERS.

AS WAS OUR BEING FORCED TO SHAVE ALL OF OUR FACIAL HAIR AS PART OF AN EFFORT TO STRIP AWAY OUR DIGNITY--

--OUR VERY HUMANITY.

Come on, man. no underwear?

BUT THE ALWAYS-COLORFUL JIM BEVEL HELPED KEEP IT IN PERSPECTIVE.

WHAT'S THIS HANG-UP ABOUT CLOTHES?

GANDHI WRAPPED A RAG AROUND HIS BALLS AND BROUGHT DOWN THE WHOLE BRITISH EMPIRE.

JUNE 24, 1961.

AS THE DAYS WORE ON, WE SANG TO KEEP THE MONOTONY FROM GETTING TO US.

CLINK CL-CLINK

AIN'T GONNA LET NO JIM CROW TURN ME AROUND

TURN ME AROUND, TURN ME AROUND

AIN'T GONNA LET NO JIM CROW TURN ME AROUND

I'M GONNA KEEP ON A-WALKIN', KEEP ON A-TALKIN',

dammit—

ALL RIGHT, ALL RIGHT—

IF YOU DON'T QUIT SINGIN' THEM DAMN SONGS, I'M GONNA TAKE EVERY LAST ONE-A-Y'ALL'S MATTRESSES!

that's IT with that noise!

MARCHIN' UP TO FREEDOM'S LAND

WHAT THEY'RE TRYING TO DO IS TAKE YOUR SOUL AWAY.

IT'S NOT THE MATTRESSES, IT'S YOUR SOUL-- SATAN PUT US HERE FOR FORTY DAYS AND FORTY NIGHTS TO TEMPT US WITH THE FLESH.

HE'S SAYIN' TO US, "IF YOU'LL JUST STOP YOUR SINGIN' AND BAIL OUTTA HERE, I'LL GIVE YOU ANYTHING YOU WANT-- SOFT, THICK COTTON MATTRESSES. DOWN PILLOWS. EVERYTHING.

"BE GOOD, BOYS, AND I'LL LET YOU KEEP YOUR MATTRESSES."

AND SO BEGAN "THE MATTRESS WAR."

103

WHUMP

WHUMP WHUMP whump whump

HERE. COME GET MY MATTRESS.

I'LL KEEP MY SOUL.

AINT GONNA LET NO JAIL HOUSE, LORDY, TURN ME AROUND ♫

I'M GONNA KEEP ON A-WALKIN', LORD, KEEP ON A-TALKIN', ♪ ♫ LORD,

MARCHIN' UP ♪ TO FREEDOM'S LAND ♫♫

THE ONLY HOLDOUTS WERE FRED LEONARD AND A HOWARD UNIVERSITY STUDENT NAMED STOKELY CARMICHAEL--

TO THEM, NONVIOLENCE WAS JUST A TACTIC, NOT A PERSONAL PHILOSOPHY OR A WAY OF LIFE.

hey DEPUTY--

BUT IN THE END, THEY LOST THEIR MATTRESSES, TOO.

SINCE THOSE MATTRESSES ARE SO **VALUABLE**, WHY DON'T YOU AUCTION THEM OFF AND TELL PEOPLE THAT THE FREEDOM RIDERS SLEPT THERE?

THAT WAY, AT LEAST YOU CAN GET BACK SOME OF THE MONEY THE FREEDOM RIDES ARE COSTING YOU.

AND WE'LL SING A LITTLE SONG AT YOUR AUCTION.

YOU **SHUT** YO' MOUTH, BOY.

DEPUTY TYSON, DO YOU MEAN ANYTHING DEROGATORY WHEN YOU CALL US **BOY**?

DON'T KNOW NOTHIN' 'BOUT NO 'ROGATORY. ALL I KNOW IS IF YOU BOYS DON'T STOP THAT SINGIN', Y'ALL GON' BE SINGIN' IN THE **RAIN**.

OLE BIG MAN DEPUTY TYSON SAID, "I DON'T WANNA CAUSE YOU ♪ PAIN, ♪

BUT IF YOU DON'T STOP THAT SINGIN' NOW, ♪

WHO SANG THAT?!

JIM--EARL! GET IN HERE!

YOU'LL BE SINGIN' IN THE RAIN! ♪

VOOSH

BUSES ARE A-COMING, oh YES, ♫

BUSES ARE ♪ A-COMING, oh YES,

WE WERE ONLY ALLOWED TO WRITE ONE LETTER A WEEK-- I ALWAYS MADE MINE AS LONG AS POSSIBLE.

I WROTE THE REGISTRAR BACK AT SCHOOL, EXPLAINING THAT I WOULDN'T BE ABLE TO GET BACK TO NASHVILLE FOR MY GRADUATION BECAUSE I WAS IN JAIL IN MISSISSIPPI.

BUSES ARE A-COMING, BUSES ARE A-COMING, ♫

BUSES ARE A-COMING, oh YES ♫

ALL RIGHT--

SHUT UP ALL THAT SINGING AND HOLLERING IN THERE!!

I ALSO WROTE TO THE QUAKERS TO WITHDRAW FROM THE PROGRAM IN INDIA. I DECIDED I TRULY BELONGED IN THE SOUTH.

THIS ISN'T NO PLAYHOUSE, IT'S A JAILHOUSE!!

WHAT ARE YOU GONNA DO?

PUT US IN JAIL?!

hee haw   ha ha

BETTER GET YOU READY, oh YES, ♫

BETTER GET YOU READY, oh YES--♪

BUSES ARE A-COMING, BUSES ARE A-COMING, ♫

IF-- IF I--

BUSES ARE A-COMING, ♪ oh YES.

JULY 7, 1961.

MISSISSIPPI, THOSE CHARGED WITH
BREACH OF THE PEACE, AS WE WERE,
HAD TO POST BOND WITHIN 40 DAYS
OR LOSE ANY RIGHT TO APPEAL.

THUP

SO, THREE WEEKS AND A DAY
AFTER WE'D ARRIVED,

AND WELL MORE THAN A MONTH
AFTER WE'D BEEN ARRESTED IN JACKSON,

IT WAS A COMPLETE SURPRISE TO US

WHEN BOND WAS POSTED ON OUR BEHALF

EXIT

AND WE WERE
SET FREE.

BY THE END OF THE SUMMER, DOZENS **MORE** BUSES CARRIED THE NATION'S DAUGHTERS AND SONS INTO THE HEART OF THE DEEP SOUTH TO CARRY ON THE WORK WE BEGAN.

THE FARE WAS PAID IN BLOOD, BUT THE FREEDOM RIDES STIRRED THE NATIONAL CONSCIOUSNESS AND AWOKE THE HEARTS AND MINDS OF A GENERATION.

THE FEDERAL GOVERNMENT RESPONDED. ATTORNEY GENERAL ROBERT KENNEDY AND THE JUSTICE DEPARTMENT PETITIONED THE INTERSTATE COMMERCE COMMISSION (ICC) FOR A RULING TO ENFORCE THE SUPREME COURT'S DECISION IN <u>BOYNTON</u>, AND IT CAME ON SEPTEMBER 22nd, 1961.

WE WERE BECOMING A **NATIONAL** MOVEMENT.

AFTER WE WERE RELEASED FROM PARCHMAN, I WENT BACK TO NASHVILLE, WHERE THE NATIONAL ATTENTION HAD CAUSED OUR NUMBERS TO SWELL.

THE SUCCESS OF OUR CAMPAIGN TO DESEGREGATE THE MOVIE THEATERS THERE LED US TO SHIFT OUR EFFORTS FROM INTEGRATION OF FACILITIES TO FAIR EMPLOYMENT PRACTICES, AS PART OF WHAT WE CALLED "OPERATION OPEN CITY."

H.G. HILL ST...
...LERMAN SHOE

THIS TIME WE WERE JOINED BY A NUMBER OF PEOPLE FROM OUT OF TOWN, MOSTLY NORTHERNERS COMING OR GOING FROM THE FREEDOM RIDES.

HEY--

SO YOU WANNA BE BLACK?

THUGS WERE HIRED TO HARASS US.

WELL, TAKE THIS!

PSHHHHHHTTTT

thank you.

I DEEPLY BELIEVE THAT OUR DISCIPLINE PAVED THE ROAD TO OUR SUCCESS.

BUT I WAS STARTING TO SEE THAT DISCIPLINE ERODE.

WHAT ARE YOU LOOKING AT?!

I LOST COUNT OF THE NUMBER OF TIMES I HAD TO TAKE SOMEONE ASIDE.

WHAT ARE YOU DOING?!

THAT'S WHAT I THOUGHT.

ONE OF THE PEOPLE PASSING THROUGH TOWN WHO ACTED OUT THE MOST WAS STOKELY CARMICHAEL.

STOKELY LATER SAID HE NEVER SAW IT AS HIS RESPONSIBILITY TO BE THE MORAL AND SPIRITUAL RECLAMATION OF SOME RACIST THUG.

THAT IS NOT HOW WE PROTEST IN NASHVILLE!

BUT HIS BEHAVIOR WAS THREATENING TO DERAIL OUR EFFORTS.

OUR CENTRAL COMMITTEE HELD A MEETING, AND THE RESPONSIBILITY FELL TO JIM LAWSON TO INFORM STOKELY OF THE DECISION.

THE COMMITTEE WOULD LIKE TO OFFER YOU AN INVITATION TO CONTINUE YOUR PROTEST ACTIVITIES...

...ELSEWHERE.

112

IN JUNE OF 1961, ROBERT KENNEDY SUGGESTED TO DIANE NASH AND OTHERS THAT IT WOULD BE A BETTER DECISION FOR US, IN THE LONG RUN, TO FOCUS ON REGISTERING BLACK VOTERS.

I BELIEVED OUR DIRECT ACTION CAMPAIGNS WERE WORKING, AND MANY WITHIN THE MOVEMENT WERE UPSET AT THE MERE SUGGESTION. BUT BY THE END OF 1961, DR. KING GAVE THE IDEA HIS FULL ENDORSEMENT.

THE CENTRAL FRONT IS THAT OF **SUFFRAGE**. IF WE IN THE SOUTH CAN WIN THE RIGHT TO VOTE, IT WILL PLACE IN OUR HANDS MORE THAN AN ABSTRACT RIGHT--

IT WILL GIVE US THE CONCRETE TOOL WITH WHICH WE, **OURSELVES**, CAN CORRECT INJUSTICE.

THERE WAS A GREAT D I V I D E WITHIN SNCC.

A COMPROMISE SUGGESTED BY ELLA BAKER WAS AGREED TO, CREATING TWO WINGS--

ONE, FOCUSED ON DIRECT ACTION, WAS LED BY DIANE NASH. THE OTHER, FOCUSED ON VOTER REGISTRATION, WAS LED BY CHARLIE JONES.

A BIRD NEEDS TWO WINGS TO FLY.

A PLAN QUICKLY TOOK SHAPE FOR SNCC TO SEND FIELD SECRETARIES INTO COMMUNITIES THROUGHOUT THE SOUTH TO ORGANIZE AND REGISTER AMERICA'S BLACK VOTE.

WHEN AMZIE MOORE, A FILLING STATION OWNER AND LOCAL ORGANIZER FROM CLEVELAND, MISSISSIPPI, CAME TO OUR SNCC MEETING AND ASKED US TO SEND HELP,

BOB MOSES, A SOFT-SPOKEN 26-YEAR-OLD FROM HARLEM WITH A GRADUATE DEGREE IN PHILOSOPHY FROM HARVARD, WAS THE HELP THAT ARRIVED.

(CLEVELAND WASN'T FAR FROM MONEY, MISSISSIPPI, WHERE JUST SIX YEARS EARLIER EMMETT TILL'S MUTILATED BODY WAS PULLED FROM THE WATERS OF THE TALLAHATCHIE.)

NO STATE SHOWED US WHAT WE WERE UP AGAINST MORE THAN MISSISSIPPI. NEARLY **90 PERCENT** OF THE STATE'S BLACK FAMILIES LIVED BELOW THE POVERTY LINE, AND ONLY **5 PERCENT** OF ELIGIBLE BLACK VOTERS WERE REGISTERED.

IN MANY COUNTIES, THERE WERE **NONE**.

THE GOOD LORD WAS THE ORIGINAL **SEGREGATIONIST**.

HE PUT THE NEGRO IN AFRICA, SEPARATED HIM FROM ALL OTHER RACES.

(GOVERNOR ROSS BARNETT, 1960-1964)

IN LIBERTY, MISSISSIPPI, A LOCAL DEL... ...
NAMED HERBERT LEE WHO STARTED WORKING
WITH BOB MOSES TO HELP REGISTER VOTERS
WAS SHOT DEAD BY E.H. HURST--

A MEMBER OF THE MISSISSIPPI
STATE LEGISLATURE.

HURST CLAIMED LEE HAD
ATTACKED HIM WITH A TIRE IRON,
AND SO HURST SHOT HIM
THROUGH THE HEAD.

NOT GUILTY BY
REASON OF
JUSTIFIABLE
HOMICIDE.

THE SOLE BLACK WITNESS LATER SAID
HE LIED IN TESTIMONY BECAUSE HE
WAS SCARED FOR HIS OWN LIFE.

BOB MOSES, CHARLES MᶜDEW,
AND A WHITE SNCC MEMBER
FROM ALABAMA NAMED BOB
ZELLNER LED A PROTEST MARCH
IN RESPONSE TO THE VERDICT.

THEY WERE BEATEN BY A MOB
BEFORE BEING ARRESTED ALONG
WITH 119 LOCAL STUDENTS.

JUSTICE FOR HERBERT LEE

THE PROTESTORS WERE SENTENCED
TO FOUR MONTHS IN PRISON.

MEANWHILE --

I ENROLLED AT FISK UNIVERSITY AND WAS ELECTED CHAIRMAN OF THE NASHVILLE MOVEMENT, BUT BY THEN DIANE AND BEVEL WERE WORKING DOWN IN JACKSON, AND MOST EVERYONE FROM THOSE EARLY MEETINGS WITH JIM LAWSON HAD MOVED ON.

I FELT A LITTLE LIKE AN OUTSIDER.

A NUMBER OF PROFESSORS, AND EVEN SOME OF MY CLASSMATES, THOUGHT I WAS A LITTLE ODD -- AND I **DID** TAKE A LIGHT COURSE LOAD TO FOCUS ON MY PRIORITY, THE MOVEMENT.

BUT I WILL NEVER FORGET GATHERING ONE AFTERNOON THAT NOVEMBER TO GO DOWNTOWN FOR A DEMONSTRATION.

whimpe pant-pant

woof! woof!

ARF!

HOWWW

ARF!

WE WERE GETTING SET TO DRIVE OVER TO FIRST BAPTIST WHEN WE HEARD A COMMOTION.

woof woof! whimper whimper RUFF!

I WAS SHOCKED TO SEE THESE YOUNG BLACK FRATERNITY MEN SWEPT UP LIKE THIS, AT THE VERY MOMENT THAT PEOPLE THEIR OWN AGE WERE RISKING THEIR LIVES.

IN APRIL 1962, **SNCC** HELD A CONFERENCE IN ATLANTA TO OBSERVE ITS SECOND ANNIVERSARY.

Welcome S.N.C.C. Conference
APRIL-27-29
ATLANTA STUDENT MOVEMENT

IT WAS INCREDIBLE TO SEE HOW DRASTICALLY THE ORGANIZATION HAD CHANGED IN SUCH A SHORT TIME.

BERNARD, BEVEL, DIANE, AND OTHERS WERE NOW GONE. IN THEIR PLACE ROSE NEW VOICES--

STOKELY CARMICHAEL, JIM FORMAN, CHARLES SHERROD, RUBY SMITH, AND WHITE ACTIVISTS FROM LEFTIST GROUPS SUCH AS THE SOUTHERN CONFERENCE EDUCATIONAL FUND AND STUDENTS FOR A DEMOCRATIC SOCIETY (SDS).

OUR CAUSE REMAINED THE SAME, BUT OUR **METHODS** WERE IN QUESTION.

WE FORGET TOO SOON THE JAILINGS AND BEATINGS SUFFERED BY OUR BROTHERS AND SISTERS FIGHTING EVERY DAY.

MORE THAN A FEW OF THE 250 SNCC REPRESENTATIVES IN ATLANTA THAT WEEKEND ARGUED THAT IT SHOULD BE ACCEPTABLE TO **STRIKE BACK** IF YOU'RE HIT.

APRIL-27-29
ANTA STUDENT MOVEMEN

IF WE ARE MET WITH VIOLENCE, WE MUST BE ABLE TO **DEFEND** OURSELVES.

JIM LAWSON WOULD **NEVER** ACCEPT SUCH A POSITION, BUT HE WASN'T THERE TO OFFER HIS OWN. FOR THE FIRST TIME, LAWSON, WHO HAD BEEN SO CRUCIAL TO THE CREATION OF **SNCC** -- THE VERY **AUTHOR** OF THE STATEMENT OF PURPOSE PRINTED ON THE CONFERENCE'S BROCHURE --

-- WAS NOT INVITED TO PARTICIPATE.

STUDENT NONVIOLENT COORDINATING COMMITTEE

STATEMENT OF PURPOSE

We affirm the philosophical or religious ideal of nonviolence as the foundation of our purpose, the presupposition of our faith, and the manner of our action. Nonviolence as it grows from Judaic-Christian traditions seeks a social order of justice permeated by love. Integration of human endeavor represents the crucial first step towards such a society.

Through nonviolence, courage displaces fear; love transforms hate. Acceptance dissipates prejudice; hope ends despair. Peace dominates war; faith reconciles doubt. Mutual regard cancels enmity. Justice for all overthrows injustice. The redemptive community supersedes systems of gross social immorality.

Love is the central motif of nonviolence. Love is the force by which God binds man to Himself and man to man. Such love goes to the extreme; it remains loving and forgiving even in the midst of hostility. It matches the capacity of evil to inflict suffering with an even more enduring capacity to absorb evil, all the while persisting in love.

By appealing to conscience and standing on the moral nature of human existence, nonviolence nurtures the atmosphere in which reconciliation and justice become actual possibilities.

EVERYONE KNEW I STOOD WITH JIM WHEN IT CAME TO NONVIOLENCE,

BUT THE FACT THAT I'D BEEN ARRESTED AND BEATEN AND JAILED SO MANY TIMES HELD A LOT OF WEIGHT WITH MY **SNCC** COLLEAGUES, OLD AND NEW.

SO AT THE SAME TIME AS JIM LAWSON WAS SHUNNED, I WAS ELECTED TO SNCC'S EXECUTIVE COORDINATING COMMITTEE.

ALBANY, GEORGIA.

THAT SUMMER, THE VIOLENCE CONTINUED TO ESCALATE.

NOK NOK

excuse me, SHERIFF--

MY NAME IS C.B. KING. I'M AN ATTORNEY HERE TO REPRESENT BILL HANSEN.

HE'S A SNCC STAFFER WHO WAS ARRESTED DURING

KRAK

THERE WERE BEATINGS.

AND THERE WERE SHOOTINGS.

POK! POK!

FOUR HOMES OF ALBANY-AREA VOTER REGISTRATION ORGANIZERS WERE RIDDLED WITH BULLETS.

POK POK

BLAM BLAM VAM VAM

A FEW NIGHTS LATER, THREE SHOTGUN BLASTS WERE FIRED INTO A HOME WHERE CHARLES SHERROD WAS SLEEPING.

CAIRO, ILLINOIS.

NEAR THE END OF THE SUMMER OF 1962, I WAS LEADING A PROTEST AT THE CAIRO SWIMMING POOL, WHICH HAD REMAINED **SEGREGATED** DESPITE OUR WEEKS OF DEMONSTRATION.

DANNY LYON, A NEW STAFF PHOTOGRAPHER FOR SNCC-- WE CALLED HIM **DANDELION**-- WAS THERE THAT DAY.

WHITES ONLY PLEASE

CLICK CLICK

AS WE KNELT AND PRAYED, DANNY SNAPPED A PHOTOGRAPH.

THAT PICTURE BECAME PROBABLY THE MOST POPULAR POSTER OF THE MOVEMENT.

WHAT A LOT OF PEOPLE **DON'T** KNOW IS WHAT HAPPENED JUST AFTER THAT PHOTO WAS TAKEN.

RRRRR

outta the way!!

he isn't stopping

THAT SEPTEMBER, THE NATION WATCHED AS MORE THAN **300** U.S. MARSHALS WERE WOUNDED TRYING TO PROTECT JAMES MEREDITH AS HE BECAME THE FIRST AFRICAN-AMERICAN TO ENROLL AT THE UNIVERSITY OF MISSISSIPPI.

IN NOVEMBER, I ATTENDED A SNCC CONFERENCE IN NASHVILLE.

THOSE MOBS DOWN IN MISSISSIPPI MAKE YOUR PROTESTS **HERE** LOOK LIKE SMALL POTATOES, JOHN.

HE WASN'T WRONG.

AS PART OF THE CONFERENCE, WE STAGED A DEMONSTRATION AT THE **TIC-TOC**, A SEGREGATED RESTAURANT.

BUT THIS PROTEST LACKED DISCIPLINE--

YOUNG MAN, WE DON'T ALLOW SMOKING HERE.

SOMETHING I WAS SEEING MORE AND MORE OFTEN.

square.

STUBBS

AND IT WASN'T THE ONLY PROBLEM FESTERING WITHIN SNCC.

BY THE END OF 1962, YOU HEARD PEOPLE QUESTIONING WHETHER SNCC SHOULD EVEN BE A MULTI-RACIAL ORGANIZATION.

JANUARY 14, 1963.
ALABAMA STATE CAPITOL.

KLOP

KLOP

KLOP

INAUGURATION OF **GEORGE CORLEY WALLACE, JR.,** 45th GOVERNOR OF ALABAMA

TODAY I HAVE STOOD WHERE ONCE JEFFERSON DAVIS STOOD, AND TOOK AN OATH TO MY PEOPLE.

EVEN AS WALLACE WAS SPEAKING THAT DAY, DR. KING'S ORGANIZATION, THE **SOUTHERN CHRISTIAN LEADERSHIP CONFERENCE** (SCLC), HELD A MEETING TO DECIDE WHAT TO DO.

IT IS VERY APPROPRIATE THEN, THAT FROM THIS CRADLE OF THE CONFEDERACY, THE VERY **HEART** OF THE GREAT ANGLO-SAXON SOUTHLAND, THAT TODAY WE SOUND THE DRUM FOR FREEDOM, AS HAVE OUR GENERATIONS OF FOREBEARS BEFORE US HAVE DONE, TIME AND TIME AGAIN THROUGHOUT **HISTORY.**

LET US RISE TO THE CALL OF FREEDOM-LOVING BLOOD THAT IS IN US, AND SEND OUR ANSWER TO THE **TYRANNY** THAT CLANKS ITS CHAINS UPON THE SOUTH.

IN THE NAME OF THE GREATEST PEOPLE THAT HAVE EVER TROD THIS EARTH, I DRAW THE LINE IN THE DUST,

THEY NEEDED A NEW **TARGET**--

THEY "NEEDED A VICTORY", AS FRED SHUTTLESWORTH PUT IT.

AND TOSS THE GAUNTLET BEFORE THE FEET OF **TYRANNY.**

AND I SAY--

SEGREGATION TODAY,

WHILE WE HAD MADE PROGRESS ELSEWHERE, ONE CITY CONTINUED TO EARN ITS LABEL AS "THE **MOST** SEGREGATED CITY IN THE SOUTH", SUBJECT TO SO MUCH VIOLENCE THAT IT WAS NICKNAMED "BOMBINGHAM."

SHUTTLESWORTH MADE A PROMISE THAT AFTERNOON TO DR. KING: "I ASSURE YOU," HE SAID, "IF YOU COME TO BIRMINGHAM, THIS MOVEMENT WILL NOT ONLY GAIN PRESTIGE--"

SEGREGATION TOMORROW,

SEGREGATION FOREVER.

"--BUT IT WILL REALLY **SHAKE** THIS COUNTRY."

ABA

APRIL 9, 1963 --
BIRMINGHAM, AL.

AND SO **THE BIRMINGHAM CAMPAIGN** BEGAN THE FIRST WEEK OF APRIL.

DR. KING AND **SCLC** BROUGHT IN PEOPLE FROM ALL CORNERS OF THE MOVEMENT. DIANE AND BEVEL WENT TO HELP ORGANIZE VOLUNTEERS AND **TRAIN** THEM IN OUR TECHNIQUES.

EVEN **AL HIBBLER**, A FAMOUS JAZZ SINGER WHO HAPPENED TO BE BLIND, JOINED THE PROTESTS.

WE COULD _NEVER_ JUST LEAVE A BLIND MAN ALONE ON A STREET CORNER...

THE NEXT DAY.

Loveman's

NOT MUCH HAD CHANGED IN THE TWO YEARS SINCE THE FREEDOM RIDE CAME THROUGH BIRMINGHAM...

BULL CONNOR HAD RUN FOR MAYOR, AND LOST... BUT HE STILL CONTROLLED THE CITY'S POLICE, AND HE WAS STILL A BULLY.

HE WAS ERRATIC,

IRRESPONSIBLE,

AND JUST PLAIN MEAN.

NIGGER.

I'M TAKING YOUR SIGN--

AND I'M TAKING YOUR EYES AWAY FROM YOU.

HEY--

BACK AGAINST THE WALL!

DON'T TELL ME TO GET BACK AGAINST THE WALL.

I'M A FREE MAN.

YOU CAN'T WORK, AND ANYONE WHO GOES TO JAIL HAS TO EARN HIS KEEP. YOU CAN'T DO ANYTHING--

EVEN ENTERTAIN.

i'll be back tomorrow.

NIGGER, YOU JUST DON'T KNOW WHEN TO QUIT.

IT WAS ONLY A MATTER OF TIME BEFORE BULL CONNOR WENT TOO FAR, AND WHEN HE DID, THE WORLD WOULD BE WATCHING.

AFTER WEEKS OF NIGHTLY MASS MEETINGS TO COORDINATE THE PROTESTS, DR. KING ANNOUNCED THAT HE WOULD PERSONALLY LEAD THE NEXT MARCH.

8:30 P.M.-- ST. JAMES AME CHURCH.

WE ARE NOT HERE TO DO SOMETHING FOR YOU, BUT TO DO SOMETHING WITH YOU. WE WILL MARCH THROUGH THE STREETS OF BIRMINGHAM WITH YOU. EVERYONE IN THE MOVEMENT MUST LIVE A SACRIFICIAL LIFE.

...FOR A MOVE FOR FREEDOM.

I CAN'T THINK OF A BETTER DAY THAN GOOD FRIDAY...

FRIDAY, APRIL 12, 1963. ZION HILL BAPTIST CHURCH-- BIRMINGHAM, AL.

all right folks, we're moving out! remember to li--

THERE HE GOES, JUST LIKE JESUS.

CONNOR HAD OBTAINED A COURT ORDER FROM THE STATE PROHIBITING ALL PROTEST ACTIVITIES, AND SET THE BOND AT EIGHT TIMES THE NORMAL MAXIMUM.

EVERYONE KNEW THAT THIS MARCH WOULD MEAN JAIL TIME.

SOME WERE CONCERNED THAT THE CAMPAIGN WOULD COLLAPSE IF DR. KING WENT TO PRISON.

STOP THEM
THERE.

HALT!

ERRRT

SCREE

CLIK

CLIK CLIK

PFASH!

WHEN DR. KING WAS ARRESTED
ON GOOD FRIDAY, HE WAS
CRITICIZED BY SOME OF THE
AREA'S LIBERAL AND MODERATE
WHITE LEADERSHIP FOR STOKING
CONFLICT BY LEADING THESE
DEMONSTRATIONS.

HIS RESPONSE, WRITTEN ON SCRAPS OF
PAPER AND SMUGGLED OUT OF HIS CELL,
WAS THE "LETTER FROM BIRMINGHAM JAIL."

"...I SUBMIT THAT AN INDIVIDUAL WHO BREAKS A LAW
THAT CONSCIENCE TELLS HIM IS **UNJUST**, AND
WHO WILLINGLY ACCEPTS THE PENALTY OF IMPRISONMENT
IN ORDER TO AROUSE THE CONSCIENCE OF THE
COMMUNITY OVER ITS INJUSTICE, IS IN REALITY
EXPRESSING THE HIGHEST **RESPECT** FOR LAW."

WHILE DR. KING WAS IN JAIL, **JIM BEVEL**, WHO HAD LEFT **SNCC** AND JOINED **SCLC**, SET OUT TO ORGANIZE AND TRAIN BIRMINGHAM'S **CHILDREN**.

WHAT KINDA MOVEMENT ARE Y'ALL TRYING TO RUN HERE?!

YOU GUYS ARE RUNNING A **SCAM** MOVEMENT.

BEVEL WENT INTO BLACK SCHOOLS AND CHURCHES, USING THE **NBC WHITE PAPER** DOCUMENTARY "THE NASHVILLE SIT-IN STORY"-- FOR WHICH WE HAD BEEN INTERVIEWED BACK IN 1960-- TO TEACH HUNDREDS OF **TEENAGERS** THE TECHNIQUES OF NONVIOLENCE.

IN A MOVEMENT, YOU **DON'T** DEAL WITH THE PRESS--

YOU ACT LIKE THERE **IS** NO PRESS. OTHERWISE YOU END UP STAGING IT.

A MOVEMENT IS WHEN PEOPLE ACTUALLY DO IT OUT OF **CONVICTION.**

YOUNG PEOPLE IDENTIFY MORE STRONGLY THAN ANYONE ELSE WITH THE **WHOLE** CONCEPT OF FREEDOM.

SOME NEGROES DON'T **WANT** TO GET WELL. IF THEY DID, THEY WOULD HAVE TO COMPETE WITH THE WHITE MAN.

THERE ARE **SOME** NEGROES WHO WANT SEGREGATION AS MUCH AS **BULL CONNOR.**

THE NEGRO HAS BEEN SITTING HERE DEAD FOR **THREE HUNDRED YEARS.**

YOUNG PEOPLE, AS WE KNEW VERY WELL, ARE WILLING TO RISK **EVERYTHING** FOR THE CAUSE.

IT'S TIME HE GOT UP AND <u>WALKED.</u>

LOVE T

EQUALITY

MAY 2, 1963--
16th STREET BAPTIST CHURCH.

ANOTHER HOT ONE!

KIDS, THERE'S GONNA BE A PARTY AT THE PARK--

SO BRING YOUR TOOTHBRUSHES, BECAUSE LUNCH WILL BE SERVED!

BLACK RADIO STATIONS HELPED COORDINATE THE PROTESTS WITH CODED ANNOUNCEMENTS.

SQUEEK

hey, FRED-- uh...

...how many more HAVE you got?

NEARLY A THOUSAND OF BIRMINGHAM'S BLACK CHILDREN WERE ARRESTED THAT DAY.

IT WAS AN **EMBARRASSMENT** TO THE CITY.

MAY 3, 1963.

BULL CONNOR WAS DETERMINED **NOT** TO LET THE PROTESTS CONTINUE.

THE NEXT DAY, WHEN THE CHILDREN MARCHED AGAIN, HE SWORE HE WOULD MAKE NO ARRESTS.

here they come.

gimme that horn, mayor.

DO **NOT** CROSS--

IF YOU COME ANY FURTHER,

WE **WILL** TURN THE FIRE HOSES ON YOU!

THESE DEMONSTRATIONS WARRANT POLICE ACTION, NOT THIS KIND OF--

TURN 'EM ON, OR GO HOME.

I WATCHED THE IMAGES ON TELEVISION THAT NIGHT...

...AND LIKE THE REST OF AMERICA, I WAS ABSOLUTELY STUNNED BY WHAT I SAW.

IT WAS UNBELIEVABLE.

IT LOOKED LIKE FOOTAGE FROM A WAR.

IN NASHVILLE WE MADE SURE THEY WERE SEEN, AND OUR RANKS GREW IMMEDIATELY BECAUSE OF IT.

IF THEY'RE STANDING UP TO FIRE HOSES AND DOGS DOWN THERE,

THE LEAST I CAN DO IS MARCH OUTSIDE A RESTAURANT UP HERE.

A WEEK AFTER THE ATTACK ON THOSE CHILDREN, AN ACCORD WAS REACHED IN BIRMINGHAM. THE CITY PROMISED TO TAKE STEPS TOWARD DESEGREGATION AND FAIR HIRING PRACTICES-- THE SAME GOALS WE WERE WORKING TOWARD IN NASHVILLE--

AND THE DEMONSTRATIONS CEASED.

JUNE 12, 1963.
FIRST BAPTIST CHURCH,
NASHVILLE, TN

and I just don't understand how Smith...

what happened?!

a field secretary for the NAACP down in Jackson,

MEDGAR EVERS--

HE WAS COMING HOME FROM A MEETING,

WALKING UP HIS DRIVEWAY,

AND THEY **SHOT** HIM.

who... who shot him?

:sniff: no one knows.

they said it was a SNIPER.

THEY CAN GET **ANYONE**. YOU'LL NEVER SEE IT COMING.

ONE DAY YOU PARK YOUR CAR IN THE DRIVEWAY AND YOU GO INSIDE, AND YOU'RE **FINE**. THE NEXT DAY, YOU COME HOME AND... YOU NEVER MAKE IT TO YOUR DOOR.

JUST LIKE THAT.

LAST NIGHT, PRESIDENT KENNEDY ADDRESSED THE NATION IN RESPONSE TO RECENT EVENTS IN BIRMINGHAM, ALABAMA AND ELSEWHERE:

THE FIRES OF FRUSTRATION AND DISCORD ARE BURNING IN EVERY CITY, NORTH **AND** SOUTH.

WE FACE, THEREFORE, A **MORAL CRISIS** AS A COUNTRY AND AS A PEOPLE. IT **CANNOT** BE MET BY REPRESSIVE POLICE ACTION. IT CANNOT BE LEFT TO INCREASED DEMONSTRATIONS ON THE STREETS. IT CANNOT BE **QUIETED** BY TOKEN MOVES OR TALKS.

--THE EVENTS IN BIRMINGHAM AND ELSEWHERE HAVE SO INCREASED THE CRIES FOR EQUALITY THAT NO CITY OR STATE LEGISLATIVE BODY CAN PRUDENTLY IGNORE THEM.

IT IS TIME TO **ACT** IN CONGRESS, IN YOUR STATE AND LOCAL LEGISLATIVE BODIES-- IN ALL OF OUR **DAILY LIVES**...

A GREAT CHANGE IS AT HAND, AND OUR TASK-- OUR **OBLIGATION** -- IS TO MAKE THAT REVOLUTION, THAT CHANGE, PEACEFUL AND CONSTRUCTIVE FOR ALL.

ALMOST LOST THAT WEEK WAS DR. KING'S ANNOUNCEMENT ON JUNE 11th OF PLANS FOR A **MASSIVE MARCH** TO TAKE PLACE LATER THAT SUMMER...

... IN **WASHINGTON, D.C.**

JUNE 14, 1963-- outside MURFREESBORO, TN.

TWO DAYS LATER, I RECEIVED A TELEGRAM FROM SNCC HEADQUARTERS, SAYING CHUCK McDEW WAS **RESIGNING** AS CHAIRMAN,

AND THAT I SHOULD HURRY TO ATLANTA FOR AN "EMERGENCY" MEETING OF THE COORDINATING COMMITTEE.

IT SEEMED STRANGE TO ME--

141

SCREEE!

I SAW MYSELF AS A **DOER.** I NEVER HAD ANY THOUGHTS OF BEING CHAIRMAN.

THERE WERE NO SEATBELTS IN THAT CAR, BUT INCREDIBLY NONE OF US WERE SERIOUSLY HURT.

Rzzzzzz

WE MADE IT, EVENTUALLY.
ANOTHER CAR WAS SENT TO PICK US UP.

AND I WAS ELECTED **CHAIRMAN** OF SNCC.

"SO HELP YOU GOD?"

SO HELP ME GOD.

CONGRATULATIONS, MR. PRESIDENT.

JUNE, 1963.

AS CHAIRMAN OF SNCC, I HAD TO WORK AT THE SNCC HEADQUARTERS IN ATLANTA FOR A SALARY OF $10 A WEEK.

KLIK

SO I MOVED INTO A SMALL APARTMENT OVER OFF GORDON ROAD IN SOUTHWEST ATLANTA.

IT WAS A BIG CHANGE FROM THE FLOORS AND COUCHES I CALLED HOME WHILE LIVING ON THE ROAD, BUT MY NEW RESPONSIBILITIES WOULD NEVER LET ME STAY THERE FOR LONG ANYWAY.

I WAS BARELY THERE A WEEK WHEN A REPRESENTATIVE OF SNCC WAS INVITED TO THE **WHITE HOUSE** TO JOIN OTHER LEADERS, DISCUSSING PRESIDENT KENNEDY'S PROPOSED **CIVIL RIGHTS BILL** AS WELL AS HIS CONCERNS ABOUT THE ANNOUNCEMENT OF A **MARCH ON WASHINGTON.**

AMONG THE SNCC MEMBERS, THERE WASN'T MUCH INTEREST IN THE MARCH **OR** PRESIDENT KENNEDY'S BILL.

MANY THOUGHT THE MARCH WOULD BE A LAME EVENT STAGED BY CONSERVATIVE BLACK LEADERS THAT WAS PROBABLY, IN SOME WAY, CONTROLLED BY THE FEDERAL GOVERNMENT.

AS FOR THE CIVIL RIGHTS BILL-- WE COULD **NOT** SUPPORT IT.

THE KENNEDY BILL DID **NOT** GUARANTEE THE RIGHT OF **ALL** AFRICAN-AMERICANS TO VOTE. THE ADMINISTRATION TOOK THE POSITION THAT, IF YOU HAD A 6TH-GRADE EDUCATION, YOU SHOULD BE CONSIDERED **LITERATE** AND ABLE TO VOTE.

SNCC'S POSITION-- AND MINE-- WAS THAT THE **ONLY** QUALIFICATION FOR BEING ABLE TO VOTE SHOULD BE THAT OF **AGE** AND **RESIDENCE.**

HERE, JOHN. YOU'RE THE CHAIRMAN-- YOU **HAVE** TO GO.

SO I WENT.

PAN AM

THE IDEA FOR THE MARCH ON WASHINGTON
CAME FROM A. PHILIP RANDOLPH.

HE WAS A STATESMAN, A TRUE GENTLEMAN.
IN 1925 HE FOUNDED THE **BROTHERHOOD OF
SLEEPING CAR PORTERS,** AN INCREDIBLY
INFLUENTIAL CIVIL RIGHTS AND LABOR
ORGANIZATION. IF HE HAD BEEN BORN AT
ANOTHER TIME, HE COULD'VE BEEN
PRESIDENT. AND I'LL NEVER FORGET
THAT DEEP BARITONE VOICE.

MR. RANDOLPH FIRST THREATENED TO
ORGANIZE A MARCH ON THE CAPITAL
CITY IN 1941 AS HE FACED OFF WITH
PRESIDENT ROOSEVELT OVER WHETHER
OR NOT AFRICAN-AMERICAN WORKERS
WOULD BE INTEGRATED INTO THE
GROWING WAR ECONOMY.

AS A RESULT, PRESIDENT ROOSEVELT
SIGNED AN EXECUTIVE ORDER FORBIDDING
THE DEFENSE INDUSTRY FROM
DISCRIMINATION IN HIRING, AND PLANS
FOR THE MARCH WERE CANCELED.

JUNE 22, 1963 -- THE WHITE HOUSE.

THE BLACK MASSES ARE **RESTLESS**, MR. PRESIDENT.

WE ARE **GOING** TO MARCH ON WASHINGTON.

WE WANT SUCCESS IN CONGRESS, NOT JUST A **BIG SHOW** AT THE CAPITOL.

THE CIVIL RIGHTS BILL STANDS A... MUCH BETTER CHANCE IF THE NEGROES STAY **OFF** THE STREETS.

THE NEGROES ARE **ALREADY** IN THE STREETS.

THERE **WILL** BE A MARCH.

MR. RANDOLPH--

IF YOU BRING ALL THESE PEOPLE TO WASHINGTON, WON'T THERE BE VIOLENCE AND CHAOS AND DISORDER?

THERE HAVE BEEN ORDERLY, PEACEFUL, NONVIOLENT PROTESTS BEFORE.

IT WAS **UNREAL** -- I HAD ONLY BEEN CHAIRMAN OF SNCC FOR A **WEEK**, AND HERE I WAS.

THE MEETING WENT ON FOR NEARLY TWO HOURS BEFORE **DR. KING** SPOKE UP FOR THE FIRST TIME.

MR. PRESIDENT--

THIS MARCH WILL HELP **DRAMATIZE** OUR STRUGGLE, MOBILIZING SUPPORT IN PARTS OF THE COUNTRY THAT **DON'T** KNOW THE PROBLEM FIRST-HAND.

I THINK IT WILL SERVE A PURPOSE.

IT MAY SEEM **ILL-TIMED** -- BUT I HAVE NEVER ENGAGED IN A DIRECT-ACTION MOVEMENT THAT DID **NOT** SEEM ILL-TIMED.

SOME PEOPLE THOUGHT **BIRMINGHAM** WAS ILL-TIMED.

INCLUDING THE ATTORNEY GENERAL.

MR. PRESIDENT, WE WILL HAVE PROBLEMS WITH OUR OWN ORGANIZATIONS IF WE DO **NOT** MARCH.

WELL,

WE ALL HAVE OUR PROBLEMS.

YOU HAVE YOUR PROBLEMS.

I HAVE MY PROBLEMS.

BUT THE PROBLEMS **WE** ARE FACING ARE MAN MADE--

AND THESE PROBLEMS MUST BE **SOLVED** BY MEN.

I SAID NOTHING AT THE MEETING, JUST LISTENED.

IT WAS NOT MY PLACE TO TALK.

MY TIME WOULD COME **LATER**.

THERE WAS ONE PERSON DELIBERATELY **NOT** INVITED THAT DAY.
MALCOLM X OF THE NATION OF ISLAM.

I **KNEW** MALCOLM. I **RESPECTED** HIM.

I **SHARED** HIS BELIEF THAT OUR STRUGGLE
WAS NOT SIMPLY IN THE COURTS, BUT
IN THE **STREETS**.

STILL, I NEVER FELT LIKE HE WAS A PART
OF THE MOVEMENT.

OUR MOVEMENT WAS ABOUT CREATING
AN OPEN, INTEGRATED SOCIETY.

AND, VIOLENCE, NO MATTER HOW JUSTIFIED,
WAS **NOT** SOMETHING I COULD ACCEPT.

BUT I COULD UNDERSTAND HIS APPEAL,
AND THE FEELINGS OF RESTLESSNESS
THAT DROVE IT.

JULY 2, 1963.

A MEETING OF THE MARCH ORGANIZERS WAS CALLED IN NEW YORK CITY. IT WAS THE FIRST TIME I HAD EVER BEEN THERE.

I'M SORRY, BUT YOU HAVE TO LEAVE. thank you.

BUT I

uh huh, yes, You TOO -- YOU CAN WAIT OUTSIDE. oh--

JOHN, YOU CAN **STAY.**

?!

I WAS SHOCKED AT THE WAY ROY WILKINS WAS ABLE TO PUSH EVERYONE AROUND.

come on in, everyone's here.

ONLY THE SIX OF US WHO MET WITH THE PRESIDENT REMAINED.

I DIDN'T KNOW IT AT THE TIME, BUT THOSE OF US IN THAT ROOM--

A. PHILIP RANDOLPH,

DR. MARTIN LUTHER KING, JR.,

ROY WILKINS of the NAACP,

JIM FARMER OF CORE,

and WHITNEY YOUNG of the URBAN LEAGUE--

-- WOULD BE FOREVER LINKED, KNOWN COLLECTIVELY AS THE "BIG SIX".

THANK YOU, ROY.

of course, Mr. Randolph.

scoot.

now--

THE DISCUSSION QUICKLY TURNED TO WHO SHOULD BE LEADING OUR EFFORTS.

AS MANY OF YOU KNOW, I BELIEVE DEEPLY IN THE NECESSITY OF A MARCH ON WASHINGTON, AND I HAVE FOR QUITE SOME TIME.

THERE IS NO ONE, IN MY ESTIMATION, MORE QUALIFIED TO ORGANIZE THIS ENDEAVOR THAN BAYARD RUSTIN.

BAYARD RUSTIN.

HE WAS ONE OF THE PEOPLE ROY WILKINS HAD ASKED TO **LEAVE**, BUT HIS TALENTS LOOMED.

A DEVOUT PACIFIST AND BRILLIANT ORGANIZER, RUSTIN HELPED WITH THE PLANNING OF RANDOLPH'S FIRST MARCH IN 1941.

BUT WILKINS AND WHITNEY YOUNG WERE **OPPOSED**.

I'M TELLING YOU, PEOPLE ARE GOING TO USE HIM **AGAINST** US.

HE'S A CONSCIENTIOUS OBJECTOR, HE'S BEEN LINKED TO THE COMMUNIST PARTY,

and, of course, there's the "MORALS" charge...

RUSTIN WAS GAY, THOUGH NO ONE SAID IT DIRECTLY. IT MADE HIM A STRATEGIC LIABILITY.

WE WERE AT AN IMPASSE UNTIL SOMEONE SUGGESTED A. PHILIP RANDOLPH LEAD THE MARCH.

YES PHIL, YOU **SHOULD** LEAD IT.

IF I DO THAT, I **WILL** CHOOSE BAYARD AS MY DEPUTY.

Well, YOU CAN DO THAT IF YOU **WANT** TO, BUT DON'T EXPECT ME TO DO ANYTHING ABOUT IT WHEN THE **TROUBLE** STARTS.

WE **NEEDED** RUSTIN. HE WAS THE ONLY PERSON WITH THE ABILITY AND CAPACITY TO ORGANIZE SUCH A **MASSIVE** MARCH.

AFTER THE MEETING, WE POSED FOR PICTURES WITH THE PRESS.

DR. KING, WHERE ARE ALL THE YOUNG PEOPLE WE KEEP HEARING ABOUT?

RIGHT THERE-- **JOHN LEWIS**, CHAIRMAN OF SNCC.

YOU SAY THIS MARCH WILL NOT INCLUDE ANY CIVIL DISOBEDIENCE OR SIT-INS. IS SNCC **BACKING AWAY** FROM ITS PROVOCATIVE TACTICS?

NO, WE WILL **NOT** CHANGE OUR TACTICS.

WE DO **NOT** WANT VIOLENCE, AND WE DO NOT ADVOCATE FOR IT--

-- BUT WE WILL **NOT** SLOW DOWN BECAUSE OF THE **POSSIBILITY**.

A FEW WEEKS LATER, I WAS INVITED TO CONTRIBUTE TO NEGOTIATIONS FOR A **SNCC**-AFFILIATED PROTEST MOVEMENT IN MARYLAND.

JULY 22, 1963--
THE JUSTICE DEPARTMENT, WASHINGTON, D.C.

DURING A BREAK, ATTORNEY GENERAL ROBERT KENNEDY PULLED ME ASIDE AND SAID SOMETHING I'LL NEVER FORGET.

A **JARRING** RIGHT HAND--

--THE **KNOCKOUT BLOW!!**

FOLLOWED BY THE LEFT UPPERCUT--

JOHN--

UP TILL THEN, MANY IN THE MOVEMENT--INCLUDING MYSELF-- HAD BEEN CRITICAL OF HIS RESPONSE TO OUR PLEAS FOR FEDERAL INTERVENTION.

YOU, THE YOUNG PEOPLE OF SNCC, HAVE EDUCATED ME.

you have CHANGED me.

now I understand.

IT SHOWED ME SOMETHING ABOUT ROBERT KENNEDY THAT I CAME TO RESPECT: EVEN THOUGH HE COULD BE A LITTLE ROUGH-- RUTHLESS, SOME WOULD SAY--

HE WAS WILLING TO LEARN,

TO GROW,

AND TO **CHANGE**.

THE ATTACKS AND CRITICISM OF THE MARCH WERE FIERCE.

ON AUGUST 13th, WITH HELP FROM **FBI** WIRETAPS, **STROM THURMOND** OF SOUTH CAROLINA SPOKE ON THE SENATE FLOOR, ATTACKING BAYARD RUSTIN FOR BEING GAY AND ENTERING HIS ARREST RECORD INTO THE CONGRESSIONAL RECORD--

-- EFFECTIVELY **OUTING** HIM TO THE ENTIRE NATION.

BUT OUR MOVEMENT WAS TAKING HOLD.

IN THE MONTHS FOLLOWING THE ANNOUNCEMENT OF PRESIDENT KENNEDY'S CIVIL RIGHTS BILL, THERE WERE MORE THAN **800** DEMONSTRATIONS IN 200 CITIES, TWENTY **THOUSAND** ARRESTS,

AND TEN **DEATHS**.

NATIONAL HEADQUARTERS
MARCH ON WASHINGTON
for JOBS & FREEDOM

WED. AUG. 28th

MY RESPONSIBILITIES AS CHAIRMAN OF SNCC TOOK ME ALL OVER THE SOUTH -- GREENWOOD, MISSISSIPPI; PINE BLUFF, ARKANSAS; SOMERVILLE, TENNESSEE; DANVILLE, VIRGINIA; SELMA, ALABAMA -- and ELSEWHERE.

THE WEEKEND BEFORE THE MARCH, I WENT TO THE MARCH'S HEADQUARTERS IN HARLEM.

BAYARD SHOWED **NO** SIGN THE ATTACKS WERE GETTING TO HIM.

WHAT ABOUT THE **LATRINES?!** WE NEED MORE--

WE CAN'T HAVE **ANY** DISORGANIZED PISSING IN THE STREETS OF WASHINGTON!

that's EXACTLY what I asked you for.

-- that's right. AND I DON'T CARE--

FOR HIM, AND FOR **ALL** OF US, IT WAS A RACE AGAINST TIME.

I STARTED WORKING ON MY SPEECH FOR THE MARCH IN ATLANTA, AT FIRST WITH SNCC STAFFER NANCY STERN, THEN WITH SNCC'S COMMUNICATIONS DIRECTOR JULIAN BOND, OUR EXECUTIVE SECRETARY JIM FORMAN, AS WELL AS PRATHIA HALL AND OTHERS HELPING ME WORK THROUGH THE EARLY DRAFTS.

BY THE TIME I GOT TO NEW YORK CITY, I WAS WORKING THROUGH THE FINAL DRAFT. THAT WEEKEND, I SAW A PHOTOGRAPH IN THE NEWSPAPER --

IT STUCK WITH ME.

PROTESTS IN RHODESIA

ONE MAN, ONE VOTE

THERE I WORKED WITH SNCC MEMBERS COURTLAND COX AND JOYCE LADNER, ONE OF BAYARD'S ASSISTANTS ELEANOR HOLMES, AND OTHERS, TO FINISH THE SPEECH.

WHEN I ARRIVED IN WASHINGTON, THE CITY WAS **VERY** TENSE.

EVERY POLICE OFFICER IN THE CITY WAS ON DUTY, ARMY PARATROOPERS HAD BEEN PUT ON ALERT, AND THE WASHINGTON SENATORS HAD CANCELED TWO HOME GAMES ON ACCOUNT OF THE MARCH.

I WAS SURPRISED TO SEE **MALCOLM X** IN MY HOTEL LOBBY.

and WHY DID YOU COME?

DING!

WHATEVER BLACK FOLKS DO, MAYBE I DON'T SUPPORT IT, BUT I'M GOING TO **BE** THERE, BROTHER--

'CAUSE THAT'S WHERE I BELONG.

KLIK

RIIINNNNG

RI...NNG

John--
come downstairs.
Must see you
at once.
-Bayard

RIIIIIINNNNNNGGGGGGG

RRII

hello?

JOHN--

IT'S BAYARD.--

WE HAVE A PROBLEM.

A PROBLEM? WHAT PROBLEM?

IT'S YOUR SPEECH--

SOME PEOPLE ARE VERY CONCERNED ABOUT SOME OF THE THINGS YOU'RE GOING TO SAY IN YOUR SPEECH. YOU NEED TO GET DOWN HERE.

WE NEED TO TALK.

I FELT IT WAS A STRONG SPEECH, AND THAT IT REPRESENTED THE POSITION OF **SNCC**.

NOK

KLIK!

good to see you, John.

hello, Bayard.

YOU--

THE HE IS

HOW CAN **ANYONE** SAY, "IN GOOD CONSCIENCE WE CANNOT SUBMIT THE ADMINISTRATION'S CIVIL RIGHTS BILL, FOR IT IS TOO LITTLE, TOO LATE.

"YOU TELL US TO **WAIT**, YOU TELL US TO BE **PATIENT**, BUT FOR MANY OF US, **PATIENCE** IS A **DIRTY** AND **NASTY** WORD"?!

THIS IS OFFENSIVE TO THE CATHOLIC CHURCH.

WHY?

PAYYY...TIENCE.

UNbelievable!

CATHOLICS **BELIEVE** IN THE WORD "PATIENCE."

FINE, WE CAN TAKE IT OUT.

good.

IT'S LATE-- THIS IS ENOUGH FOR NOW.

I'M SURE THERE WILL BE MORE, ONCE THE OTHERS HAVE SEEN YOUR SPEECH.

I WILL LISTEN, BUT I CAN'T MAKE ANY PROMISES.

GET SOME REST--

WE HAVE A BIG DAY AHEAD OF US TOMORROW.

AUGUST 28, 1963.

THE NEXT MORNING, WE HAD BREAKFAST TOGETHER BEFORE HEADING AS A GROUP
TO MEET WITH MEMBERS OF CONGRESSIONAL LEADERSHIP.

NO ONE MENTIONED MY SPEECH.

THE MEETINGS WERE QUICK.

NOTHING SUBSTANTIVE WAS DISCUSSED.

THEN WE LEARNED
THAT THE MARCH HAD STARTED
WITHOUT US.

My God, they're going..!

WE'RE SUPPOSED TO BE LEADING **THEM** !!

THERE GOES AMERICA, I THOUGHT.

JOBS FOR ALL NOW!

WE CLEARED A SPACE TO TAKE PICTURES, BUT WE WERE **NOT** AT THE FRONT OF THE MARCH.

TRUTH BE TOLD, WE COULDN'T EVEN **SEE** THE FRONT.

AS THE CROWDS GATHERED, THE PROGRAM BEGAN WITH MUSIC FROM SOME TRULY UNBELIEVABLE PERFORMERS--

MAHALIA JACKSON;

ODETTA;

JOSH WHITE;

JOAN BAEZ and BOB DYLAN;

PETER, PAUL, + MARY;

THE SNCC FREEDOM SINGERS.

WHAT **NO ONE** SAW WAS THE DRAMA UNFOLDING OVER MY SPEECH BACKSTAGE.

I JUST DON'T UNDERSTAND YOU SNCC PEOPLE!

YOU ALWAYS WANT TO BE **DIFFERENT.**

MR. WILKINS, **YOU** DON'T UNDERSTAND.

I'M **NOT** JUST SPEAKING FOR MYSELF--

YOU JUST **CAN'T SAY** "REVOLUTION" OR "MASSES".

IT'S COMMUNIST TALK.

THERE'S NOTHING **WRONG** WITH THOSE TWO WORDS-- I'VE USED THEM MANY TIMES MYSELF.

AFTER THAT, WE HAD TO **STOP**-- RANDOLPH NEEDED TO GIVE HIS SPEECH OPENING THE OFFICIAL PROGRAM.

BY THE TIME HE RETURNED, THE LIST OF OBJECTIONS HAD GROWN. COURTLAND COX AND JIM FORMAN HAD HEARD WHAT WAS HAPPENING, AND CAME TO THE TENT TO JOIN ME.

You got to listen... what we...

WHAT **IS** ALL THIS?!

IF THERE'S GONNA BE **ONE** MORE WORD CHANGED, IT'S GONNA BE OVER **MY DEAD BODY!**

hey now, charles!

I HAVE WAITED TWENTY-TWO YEARS FOR THIS.

I'VE WAITED ALL MY **LIFE** FOR THIS OPPORTUNITY.

please don't ruin it.

FINALLY, AS THE TIME FOR MY SPEECH CAME NEAR...

JOHN, WE'VE COME THIS FAR TOGETHER.

LET US **STAY** TOGETHER.

OKAY, SIR, WE'LL MAKE THE CHANGES.

I SIMPLY COULD **NOT** SAY NO TO MR. RANDOLPH.

IN THE END, MY SPEECH NO LONGER CALLED THE PRESIDENT'S BILL "TOO LITTLE, TOO LATE", NOR CALLED FOR A "MARCH THROUGH THE HEART OF DIXIE, THE WAY SHERMAN DID."

IT NO LONGER ASKED, "WHICH SIDE IS THE GOVERNMENT ON?", NOR DESCRIBED SOME POLITICAL LEADERS AS "CHEAP."

TIK
TIKKA
TIKKA

TAK
TAK
TIK

TEN MINUTES, JOHN!

BUT WHEN WE WERE FINISHED, I WAS STILL SATISFIED WITH THE SPEECH, AS WERE FORMAN AND COX.

ZZZZ-ZIIPPP!!

WE ALL AGREED THAT OUR MESSAGE WAS **NOT** COMPROMISED.

WE WANT

BROTHER JOHN LEWIS.

I SPOKE NUMBER SIX THAT DAY.

thank you, brother.

OUT OF EVERYONE WHO SPOKE AT THE MARCH,

I'M THE ONLY ONE STILL AROUND.

WE MARCH TODAY FOR JOBS AND FREEDOM, BUT WE HAVE NOTHING TO BE PROUD OF. FOR HUNDREDS AND THOUSANDS OF OUR BROTHERS ARE **NOT** HERE.

FOR THEY ARE RECEIVING STARVATION WAGES, OR NO WAGES AT **ALL**. WHILE WE STAND HERE, THERE ARE SHARECROPPERS IN THE DELTA OF MISSISSIPPI WHO ARE OUT IN THE FIELDS WORKING FOR LESS THAN **THREE DOLLARS A DAY**, TWELVE HOURS A DAY.

WHILE WE STAND HERE, THERE ARE STUDENTS IN JAIL ON TRUMPED-UP CHARGES. OUR BROTHER **JAMES FARMER**, ALONG WITH MANY OTHERS, IS ALSO IN JAIL.

WE COME HERE TODAY WITH A GREAT SENSE OF **MISGIVING**.

IT IS TRUE THAT WE SUPPORT THE ADMINISTRATION'S CIVIL RIGHTS BILL--

WE SUPPORT IT WITH GREAT **RESERVATIONS**, HOWEVER.

UNLESS **TITLE III** IS PUT IN THIS BILL, THERE IS **NOTHING** TO PROTECT THE YOUNG CHILDREN AND OLD WOMEN WHO MUST FACE **POLICE DOGS** AND **FIRE HOSES** IN THE SOUTH WHILE THEY ENGAGE IN PEACEFUL DEMONSTRATIONS.

IN ITS PRESENT FORM, THIS BILL WILL **NOT** PROTECT THE CITIZENS OF DANVILLE, VIRGINIA, WHO MUST LIVE IN CONSTANT FEAR OF A **POLICE STATE**.

IT WILL **NOT** PROTECT THE HUNDREDS AND THOUSANDS OF PEOPLE THAT HAVE BEEN ARRESTED ON TRUMPED-UP CHARGES.

WHAT ABOUT THE THREE YOUNG MEN-- **SNCC** FIELD SECRETARIES IN AMERICUS, GEORGIA-- WHO FACE THE **DEATH PENALTY** FOR ENGAGING IN PEACEFUL PROTEST?

AS IT STANDS NOW, THE VOTING SECTION OF THIS BILL WILL **NOT** HELP THE THOUSANDS OF BLACK PEOPLE WHO **WANT** TO VOTE. IT WILL **NOT** HELP THE CITIZENS OF MISSISSIPPI, OF ALABAMA AND GEORGIA, WHO ARE **QUALIFIED** TO VOTE, BUT LACK A SIXTH-GRADE EDUCATION.

"ONE MAN, ONE VOTE" IS THE AFRICAN CRY. IT IS OURS TOO-- IT MUST BE OURS!

167

WE MUST HAVE LEGISLATION THAT WILL PROTECT THE MISSISSIPPI SHARECROPPER WHO IS PUT OFF HIS FARM BECAUSE HE **DARES** TO REGISTER TO VOTE.

MY FRIENDS, LET US NOT FORGET THAT WE ARE INVOLVED IN A SERIOUS **SOCIAL REVOLUTION**--

BY AND LARGE, AMERICAN POLITICS IS DOMINATED BY POLITICIANS WHO BUILD THEIR CAREERS ON IMMORAL COMPROMISES, AND ALLY THEMSELVES WITH OPEN FORMS OF POLITICAL, ECONOMIC, AND SOCIAL **EXPLOITATION.**

WE **NEED** A BILL THAT WILL PROVIDE FOR THE HOMELESS AND **STARVING** PEOPLE OF THIS NATION.

WE **NEED** A BILL THAT WILL ENSURE THE EQUALITY OF A MAID WHO EARNS **FIVE DOLLARS A WEEK** IN A HOME OF A FAMILY WHOSE TOTAL INCOME IS $100,000 A YEAR. WE MUST HAVE A GOOD **FEPC** BILL.

THERE ARE EXCEPTIONS, OF COURSE. WE **SALUTE** THOSE.

BUT WHAT POLITICAL LEADER CAN STAND UP AND SAY, "MY PARTY IS THE PARTY OF PRINCIPLES"?

FOR THE PARTY OF **KENNEDY** IS ALSO THE PARTY OF EASTLAND. THE PARTY OF JAVITS IS ALSO THE PARTY OF **GOLDWATER.**

WHERE IS OUR PARTY?!

WHERE IS THE POLITICAL PARTY THAT WILL MAKE IT UNNECESSARY TO MARCH ON WASHINGTON?!

WHERE IS THE POLITICAL PARTY THAT WILL MAKE IT UNNECESSARY TO MARCH IN THE STREETS OF BIRMINGHAM?

WHERE IS THE POLITICAL PARTY THAT WILL PROTECT THE CITIZENS OF ALBANY, GEORGIA?

DO YOU KNOW THAT IN ALBANY, GEORGIA, NINE OF OUR LEADERS HAVE BEEN INDICTED NOT BY THE DIXIECRATS, BUT BY THE FEDERAL GOVERNMENT, FOR PEACEFUL PROTEST?

BUT WHAT DID THE FEDERAL GOVERNMENT DO WHEN ALBANY'S DEPUTY SHERIFF BEAT ATTORNEY C.B. KING AND LEFT HIM HALF-DEAD?

WHAT DID THE FEDERAL GOVERNMENT DO WHEN LOCAL POLICE OFFICIALS KICKED AND ASSAULTED THE PREGNANT WIFE OF SLATER KING,

and she lost her baby?

TO THOSE WHO HAVE SAID, "BE PATIENT AND WAIT," WE HAVE LONG SAID THAT WE CANNOT BE PATIENT.

WE DO NOT WANT OUR FREEDOM GRADUALLY, BUT WE WANT TO BE FREE NOW!

WE ARE TIRED.

WE ARE TIRED OF BEING BEATEN BY POLICEMEN.

WE ARE TIRED OF SEEING OUR PEOPLE LOCKED UP IN JAIL OVER AND OVER AGAIN.

169

WE WILL MARCH THROUGH THE SOUTH; THROUGH THE STREETS OF **JACKSON**, THROUGH THE STREETS OF **DANVILLE**, THROUGH THE STREETS OF **CAMBRIDGE**, THROUGH THE STREETS OF **BIRMINGHAM**.

BUT WE WILL MARCH WITH THE SPIRIT OF **LOVE** AND WITH THE SPIRIT OF **DIGNITY** THAT WE HAVE SHOWN HERE **TODAY**.

BY THE FORCE OF OUR DEMANDS, OUR DETERMINATION, AND OUR NUMBERS, WE SHALL SPLINTER THE SEGREGATED SOUTH INTO A THOUSAND PIECES, AND PUT THEM TOGETHER IN THE IMAGE OF GOD AND DEMOCRACY.

WE MUST SAY: "WAKE UP, AMERICA!"

"WAKE UP!!

FOR WE CANNOT STOP,

AND WE WILL **NOT** AND **CANNOT** BE PATIENT.

DR. KING WAS THE DAY'S LAST SPEAKER.

HE STARTED SLOW. I'D HEARD HIM SPEAK
MANY TIMES. HIS CADENCE WAS SO FAMILIAR TO ME.

BUT AS HE FOUND HIS STRENGTH,
HIS **POWER**, HE TRANSFORMED THE
STEPS OF THE LINCOLN MEMORIAL
INTO A MODERN-DAY **PULPIT**.

HIS WORDS CARRIED THROUGH THE AIR
LIKE **ARROWS**... MOVING TO A CLIMACTIC
REFRAIN THE WORLD WOULD
NEVER FORGET.

TELL 'EM ABOUT
THE <u>DREAM</u>,
MARTIN.

IN THOSE MOMENTS, DR. KING MADE PLAIN ALL OF OUR HOPES, OUR ASPIRATIONS...

EVERYTHING WE SOUGHT THROUGH THE BEATINGS AND THE BLOOD, THROUGH THE TRIUMPHS AND FAILURES,

EVERYTHING WE DARED TO IMAGINE ABOUT A NEW AMERICA, A BETTER AMERICA,

IN WHICH EACH OF GOD'S CHILDREN CAN LIVE IN A SOCIETY THAT MAKES LOVE ITS HIGHEST VIRTUE.

AFTER THE PROGRAM WAS OVER, ALL OF THE SPEAKERS WERE INVITED TO THE WHITE HOUSE TO MEET WITH PRESIDENT KENNEDY.

GOOD TO SEE YOU--

YOU DID A GOOD JOB.

THANK YOU, MR. PRESIDENT.

I HEARD YOUR SPEECH.

AND YOU HAD A DREAM.

IT WAS THE LAST TIME I SAW PRESIDENT KENNEDY ALIVE.

JANUARY 20, 2009.

THANK YOU.

MY FELLOW CITIZENS...

...I STAND HERE TODAY HUMBLED BY THE TASK BEFORE US, GRATEFUL FOR THE TRUST YOU HAVE BESTOWED --

10:22 AM,
SUNDAY, SEPTEMBER 15, 1963.

YOUTH SUNDAY.

MINDFUL OF
THE SACRIFICES BORNE
BY OUR ANCESTORS.

SIXTEENTH STREET BAPTIST CHURCH-- BIRMINGHAM, AL.

WWEEEEEEEEEEOOOOOO

WWWW

WWWWEEEEOOOOWWWWWWW

Denise?
Addie?

X
end
book
two.

ACKNOWLEDGMENTS

I am deeply grateful to Andrew Aydin for all of his hard work. He had a vision, and he never gave up. I believe together we have created something truly meaningful. I want to thank Nate Powell for his unbelievable talent, kind spirit, and hard work. He is a wonderful collaborator. And I want to thank Chris Staros, Brett Warnock, Leigh Walton, Chris Ross, and everyone at Top Shelf for their openness, their support, and their powerful work.

John Lewis

I want to thank my Mom for the opportunities in my life that her hard work and sacrifice made possible. I am forever indebted to John Lewis for his remarkable life, his trust, his faith, and his friendship. I am in awe of Nate Powell's talent and grateful to work with him. I want to thank Sara for her patience and support, Vaughn for his guidance and friendship, and Dom for reminding me to have fun. I wish Jordan could see this. And thank you Mr. Parker, Mrs. Fuentes, Jacob Gillison, A.D., Professor Uchimura and all of the teachers and mentors that gave me the courage to walk this road.

Andrew Aydin

I'd like to dedicate my work on this book to the memory of Sarah Kirsch (1970–2012), whose compassion, humanity, vision, and talent deeply shaped the direction of my life from my early teenage years; to my wife Rachel, a true original and cranky do-gooder committed to helping those who need a hand; and to our amazing daughter Harper, in hopes of her growing into a world more humane, more considerate, more loving—a world she and her entire generation will inherit. Let's make the world worth it.

Nate Powell

**Dedicated to the memory of
John Seigenthaler
July 27th, 1927-July 11th, 2014**

Original Draft of SNCC Chairman John Lewis' Speech to the March

WE MARCH TODAY FOR JOBS AND FREEDOM, BUT WE HAVE NOTHING TO BE PROUD OF, for hundreds and thousands of our brothers are not here. They have no money for their transportation, for they are receiving starvation wages, or no wages at all.

In good conscience, we cannot support wholeheartedly the administration's civil rights bill, for it is too little and too late. There's not one thing in the bill that will protect our people from police brutality.

This bill will not protect young children and old women from police dogs and fire hoses, for engaging in peaceful demonstrations: This bill will not protect the citizens in Danville, Virginia, who must live in constant fear in a police state. This bill will not protect the hundreds of people who have been arrested on trumped-up charges. What about the three young men in Americus, Georgia, who face the death penalty for engaging in peaceful protest?

The voting section of this bill will not help thousands of black citizens who want to vote. It will not help the citizens of Mississippi, of Alabama and Georgia, who are qualified to vote but lack a sixth-grade education. "ONE MAN, ONE VOTE" is the African cry. It is ours, too. It must be ours.

People have been forced to leave their homes because they dared to exercise their right to register to vote. What is there in this bill to ensure the equality of a maid who earns $5 a week in the home of a family whose income is $100,000 a year?

For the first time in one hundred years this nation is being awakened to the fact that segregation is evil and that it must be destroyed in all forms. Your presence today proves that you have been aroused to the point of action.

We are now involved in a serious revolution. This nation is still a place of cheap political leaders who build their careers on immoral compromises and ally themselves with open forms of political, economic and social exploitation. What political leader here can stand up and say, "My party is the party of principles?" The party of Kennedy is also the party of Eastland. The party of Javits is also the party of Goldwater. Where is *our* party?

In some parts of the South we work in the fields from sunup to sundown for $12 a week. In Albany, Georgia, nine of our leaders have been indicted not by Dixiecrats but by the federal government for peaceful protest. But what did the federal government do when Albany's deputy sheriff beat attorney C. B. King and left him half dead? What did the federal government do when local police officials kicked and assaulted the pregnant wife of Slater King, and she lost her baby?

It seems to me that the Albany indictment is part of a conspiracy on the part of the federal government and local politicians in the interest of expediency.

I want to know, which side is the federal government on?

The revolution is at hand, and we must free ourselves of the chains of political and economic slavery.

The nonviolent revolution is saying, "We will not wait for the courts to act, for we have been waiting for hundreds of years. We will not wait for the President, the Justice Department, nor Congress, but we will take matters into our own hands and create a source of power, outside of any national structure, that could and would assure us a victory."

To those who have said, "Be patient and wait," we must say that "patience" is a dirty and nasty word. We cannot be patient, we do not want to be free gradually. We want our freedom, and we want it *now*. We cannot depend on any political party, for both the Democrats and the Republicans have betrayed the basic principles of the Declaration of Independence.

We all recognize the fact that if any radical social, political and economic changes are to take place in our society, the people, the masses, must bring them about. In the struggle, we must seek more than civil rights; we must work for the community of love, peace and true brotherhood. Our minds, souls and hearts cannot rest until freedom and justice exist for *all people*.

The revolution is a serious one. Mr. Kennedy is trying to take the revolution out of the streets and put it into the courts. Listen, Mr. Kennedy. Listen, Mr. Congressman. Listen, fellow citizens. The black masses are on the march for jobs and freedom, and we must say to the politicians that there won't be a "cooling-off" period.

All of us must get in the revolution. Get in and stay in the streets of every city, every village and every hamlet of this nation until true freedom comes, until the revolution is complete. In the Delta of Mississippi, in southwest Georgia, in Alabama, Harlem, Chicago, Detroit, Philadelphia and all over this nation, the black masses are on the march!

We won't stop now. All of the forces of Eastland, Barnett, Wallace and Thurmond won't stop this revolution. The time will come when we will not confine our marching to Washington. We will march through the South, through the heart of Dixie, the way Sherman did. We shall pursue our own "scorched earth" policy and burn Jim Crow to the ground — nonviolently. We shall fragment the South into a thousand pieces and put them back together in the image of democracy. We will make the action of the past few months look petty. And I say to you, WAKE UP AMERICA!

We will not stop. If we do not get meaningful legislation out of this Congress, the time will come when we will not confine our marching to Washington. We will march through the South, through the streets of Jackson, through the streets of Danville, through the streets of Cambridge, through the streets of Birmingham. But we will march with the spirit of love and with the spirit of dignity that we have shown here today.

By the force of our demands, our determination and our numbers, we shall splinter the segregated South into a thousand pieces and put them back together in the image of God and democracy.

We must say, "Wake up, America. *Wake up!!!*" For we cannot stop, and we *will* not be patient.

ABOUT THE AUTHORS

JOHN LEWIS is the U.S. Representative for Georgia's fifth congressional district and an American icon widely known for his role in the civil rights movement.

As a student at American Baptist Theological Seminary in 1959, Lewis organized sit-in demonstrations at segregated lunch counters in Nashville, Tennessee. In 1961, he volunteered to participate in the Freedom Rides, which challenged segregation at interstate bus terminals across the South. He was beaten severely by angry mobs and arrested by police for challenging the injustice of "Jim Crow" segregation in the South.

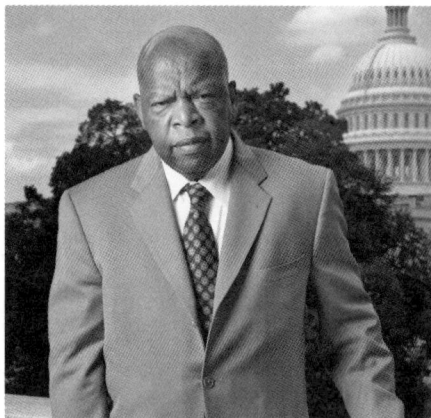

Photo by Eric Etheridge

From 1963 to 1966, Lewis was Chairman of the Student Nonviolent Coordinating Committee (SNCC). As head of SNCC, Lewis became a nationally recognized figure, dubbed one of the "Big Six" leaders of the civil rights movement. At the age of 23, he was an architect of and a keynote speaker at the historic March on Washington in August 1963.

In 1964, John Lewis coordinated SNCC efforts to organize voter registration drives and community action programs during the Mississippi Freedom Summer. The following year, Lewis helped spearhead one of the most seminal moments of the civil rights movement. Together with Hosea Williams, another notable civil rights leader, John Lewis led over 600 peaceful, orderly protesters across the Edmund Pettus Bridge in Selma, Alabama on March 7, 1965. They intended to march from Selma to Montgomery to demonstrate the need for voting rights in the state. The marchers were attacked by Alabama state troopers in a brutal confrontation that became known as "Bloody Sunday." News broadcasts and photographs revealing the senseless cruelty of the segregated South helped hasten the passage of the Voting Rights Act of 1965.

Despite physical attacks, serious injuries, and more than 40 arrests, John Lewis remained a devoted advocate of the philosophy of nonviolence. After leaving SNCC in 1966, he continued to work for civil rights, first as Associate Director of the Field Foundation, then with the Southern Regional Council, where he became Executive Director of the Voter Education Project (VEP). In 1977, Lewis was appointed by President Jimmy Carter to direct more than 250,000 volunteers of ACTION, the federal volunteer agency.

In 1981, Lewis was elected to the Atlanta City Council. He was elected to the U.S. House of Representatives in November 1986 and represented Georgia's fifth district there ever since. In 2011 he was awarded the Medal of Freedom by President Barack Obama.

Lewis' 1998 memoir *Walking with the Wind: A Memoir of the Movement* won numerous honors, including the Robert F. Kennedy, Lillian Smith, and Anisfield-Wolf Book Awards. His subsequent book, *Across That Bridge: Life Lessons and a Vision for Change*, has won the NAACP Image Award.

(From left to right): Nate Powell, Congressman John Lewis, Andrew Aydin.   Photo by Sandi Villarreal

ANDREW AYDIN, an Atlanta native, currently serves as Digital Director & Policy Advisor in the Washington, D.C., office of Rep. John Lewis. Following his master's thesis on the history and impact of the 1950s comic book *Martin Luther King & The Montgomery Story*, Aydin continues to publish and lecture about the history of comics in the civil rights movement.

Previously, he served as Communications Director and Press Secretary during Rep. Lewis' 2008 and 2010 re-election campaigns, as District Aide to Rep. John Larson (D-CT), and as Special Assistant to Connecticut Lt. Governor Kevin Sullivan. Aydin is a graduate of the Lovett School in Atlanta, Trinity College in Hartford, and Georgetown University in Washington, D.C. For more information, visit www.andrewaydin.com.

NATE POWELL is a *New York Times* best-selling graphic novelist born in Little Rock, Arkansas, in 1978. He began self-publishing at age 14, and graduated from School of Visual Arts in 2000.

His work includes *Any Empire*, *Swallow Me Whole* (Eisner and Ignatz Award winner and *LA Times* Book Prize finalist), *The Silence of Our Friends*, *The Year of the Beasts*, and Rick Riordan's *The Lost Hero*, earning a total 4 YALSA Great Graphic Novels for Teens selections and nominations for 8 Eisners and 3 Harvey Awards. In 2011, Powell discussed his work at the United Nations alongside some of the world's foremost writers of young adult fiction.

In addition to the *March* trilogy and the collection *You Don't Say*, Powell is currently writing and drawing his next book, *Cover*, slated for release in 2017. He lives in Bloomington, Indiana. You can find Powell's work at www.seemybrotherdance.org.

ALSO AVAILABLE:

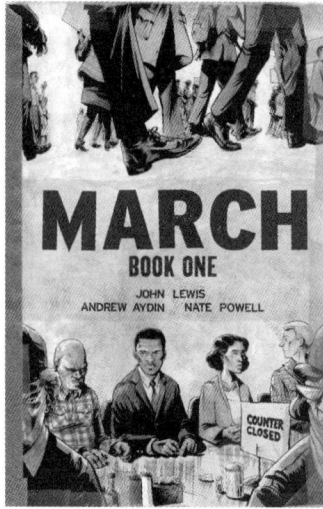

ISBN: 978-1-60309-300-2

#1 *New York Times* **and** *Washington Post* **Bestseller**
A Coretta Scott King Honor Book
Winner of the Robert F. Kennedy Book Award—Special Recognition
An ALA Notable Book
One of YALSA's Top 10 Great Graphic Novels for Teens
One of YALSA's Outstanding Books for the College Bound
One of *Reader's Digest's* **Graphic Novels Every Grown-Up Should Read**

"Congressman John Lewis has been a resounding moral voice in the quest for equality for more than 50 years, and I'm so pleased that he is sharing his memories of the Civil Rights Movement with America's young leaders. In *March*, he brings a whole new generation with him across the Edmund Pettus Bridge, from a past of clenched fists into a future of outstretched hands."

—President Bill Clinton

"A riveting and beautiful civil-rights story...Lewis's gripping memoir should be stocked in every school and shelved at every library."

—*The Washington Post*

"Essential reading...*March* is a moving and important achievement...the story of a true American superhero."

—*USA Today*

"Brave acts of civil disobedience...[give] *March* its educational value even as Powell's drawings give Lewis's crisp narration an emotional power."

—*The New York Times*

"Superbly told history."   —*Publishers Weekly* (starred review)

"An astonishingly accomplished graphic memoir that brings to life a vivid portrait of the civil rights era, Lewis' extraordinary history and accomplishments, and the movement he helped lead…Its power, accessibility and artistry destine it for awards, and a well-deserved place at the pinnacle of the comics canon."

—NPR

"A riveting chronicle of Lewis's extraordinary life…it powerfully illustrates how much perseverance is needed to achieve fundamental social change."

—O, *The Oprah Magazine*

"*March* offers a poignant portrait of an iconic figure that both entertains and edifies, and deserves to be placed alongside other historical graphic memoirs like *Persepolis* and *Maus*."

—*Entertainment Weekly*

"The civil rights movement can seem to some like a distant memory…John Lewis refreshes our memories in dramatic fashion."

—*The Chicago Tribune*

"When a graphic novel tries to interest young readers in an important topic, it often feels forced. Not so with the exhilarating *March: Book One*…Powerful words and pictures."

—*The Boston Globe*

"A powerful tale of courage and principle igniting sweeping social change, told by a strong-minded, uniquely qualified eyewitness…The heroism of those who sat and marched…comes through with vivid, inspiring clarity."

—*Kirkus Reviews* (starred review)

"Lewis's remarkable life has been skillfully translated into graphics…Segregation's insult to personhood comes across here with a visual, visceral punch. This version of Lewis's life story belongs in libraries to teach readers about the heroes of America."

—*Library Journal* (starred review)

"*March* provides a potent reminder that the sit-ins, far from being casually assembled, were well-coordinated, disciplined events informed by a rigorous philosophy… likely to prove inspirational to readers for years to come."

—*Barnes and Noble Review*

"Powell's drawings in *March* combine the epic sweep of history with the intimate personal details of memoir, and bring Lewis's story to life in a way that feels entirely unfamiliar. *March* is shaping up to be a major work of history and graphic literature."

—*Slate*

"In a new graphic memoir, the civil rights leader shows youth how to get in trouble— good trouble."

—*In These Times*

March: Book Two © 2015 John Lewis and Andrew Aydin.

Written by John Lewis and Andrew Aydin
Art by Nate Powell

Published by Top Shelf Productions
PO Box 1282
Marietta, GA 30061-1282
USA

Editor-in-Chief: Chris Staros

Top Shelf Productions is an imprint of IDW Publishing, a division of Idea and Design Works, LLC. Offices: 2765 Truxtun Road, San Diego CA 92106. Top Shelf Productions®, the Top Shelf logo, Idea and Design Works®, and the IDW logo are registered trademarks of Idea and Design Works, LLC. All Rights Reserved. With the exception of small excerpts of artwork used for review purposes, none of the contents of this publication may be reprinted without the permission of IDW Publishing. IDW Publishing does not read or accept unsolicited submissions of ideas, stories, or artwork.

Edited by Leigh Walton
Publicity by Leigh Walton (leigh@topshelfcomix.com)
Designed by Chris Ross and Nate Powell

Visit our online catalog at www.topshelfcomix.com.

Printed in Canada.

3 5 7 9 8 6 4